PEAK

Eric Sparling

Podium

Podium

To my daughter Piper

"[K2 has] just the bare bones of a name, all rock and ice and storm and abyss. It makes no attempt to sound human. It is atoms and stars. It has the nakedness of the world before the first man – or of the cindered planet after the last."

– FOSCO MARAINI

PROLOGUE

JULY 29

THE NIGHT BEFORE a summit attempt.

Teams are asleep at Camp Four. The smallest group has just three members: two professionals and a client. One of the pros is a sherpa. He rests alone in a two-man tent. Nightmares torment him.

...My son Nima...please, no...

The expedition's leader and the client share the other tent. The former sleeps deeply even at extreme altitude. His client snores prodigiously. Just breathing is a struggle for him. The air in the tent is thick despite its low oxygen content. A scent of rotting fruit and decaying vegetables pollutes the darkness. The client stops breathing, holds his breath for fifteen seconds, then gasps for air.

"...Karen..."

The client says the name twice more, the final time just a whisper. The syncopated rise and fall of his chest stabilizes. His snores return to a steady bellow. Then he sits up. Blind darkness doesn't stop his hand from homing in on his tentmate's summit bag, one of two slim packs deposited at their feet in preparation for the final push. The fingers unerringly find what they seek in its packed contents.

The man unzips the tent and ducks outside. He is wearing socks but no boots, no coat and no gloves. The temperature is startlingly cold but the man doesn't know that. He is still asleep. His thumb punches a pattern into the surface of the stolen item. Then he raises the plastic, yellow device up to his ear.

Eight seconds pass before he speaks.

"It's Phil. Yes. Put Karen on the phone."

3

PART I

CHAPTER ONE

JULY 12

THE AIR WAS clear and cold. My ascender gripped the fixed rope. It wouldn't let me fall. I slid the handle up the rope and then pulled on it. My other hand palmed the head of my ice axe. I used the tool as a cane to help propel me uphill.

I was a little nervous. I'd never been on the mountain by myself. I didn't know if my fitness was improving or I'd just grown more tolerant of pain, but the climbing felt easier than the previous times I'd been on the route.

Ivan clearly had more confidence in me. The lead guide sent me up alone from Advanced Base Camp, with only the fixed rope for company. Ang was above, at Camp One. Ivan had to wait for a load of fuel from Base Camp to make it through the icefall to ABC.

"I'll catch up," said the captain of our expedition.

The cold was bracing. It felt sharp in my lungs. Minus-twenty in the sun. It would have been murderous with any wind but the air was still. Flakes of crystal snow gleamed and even the black rock shone with optimism, as if some day spring might visit K2's forever winter, bringing alpine flowers and bees.

I must have been halfway to one when the rope took a sharp right turn.

I stopped. I wasn't feeling cold anymore. I was sweating profusely from my efforts. I didn't remember a right-angle turn. The rope was heading horizontally across the slope in the direction of a low ridge of jagged stone. I looked uphill. There was no sign of a rope or tracks.

I wouldn't forget a traverse, would I? Ang, the lead sherpa, must have changed the route. Found an easier path – safer perhaps.

I wouldn't need my ascender for the new line. If anything the rope ran slightly downhill. I attached a biner to it with a cord snapped into my harness, then started hiking across the slope in the direction of the rocks. It was tough going. The snow was deep. In a few patches it rose nearly to my hips. I resorted to a movement not unlike wading in waist-high water, except this was far more tiring.

The rope passed through a notch in the rocks. I scrambled out of the snow and onto the black stone. I followed the line along a ledge, the drop-off beneath me growing with each step until it felt like I was inching along a windowsill thirty stories up. Ice coated the rock. My crampons bit into the surface but it was easy to imagine them slipping free, my feet gliding out from under me.

7

The rope would save me. Unless it didn't. But can't think about that.

I kept my gaze averted, looking to the left where my fingers searched for hand-holds. Finally the fixed line passed behind a house-sized boulder and emerged into a snow-filled couloir. And there it stopped.

Goddammit. I looked up the narrow ravine, trying to see if the rope started again further up. Nothing.

There was no way I was unclipping to go look. Couloirs provide inviting access to higher places but they also funnel anything that falls into them. It looked sketchy. I could clearly see a line of crumbling seracs at the head of the steep canyon. Even with my scant experience I could spot such an obvious danger. Surely Ang didn't mean for me to ascend this way. I had to be on the wrong route. Nothing to do but turn around.

The windowsill was even more frightening the second time through. Forget thirty stories. One good step in the wrong direction and I'd drop two thousand feet before I touched the slope again. A new feeling skulked just below the radar of my consciousness. I knew it was there and had a good idea what it was: panic threatening to take hold.

I told myself I was safe. I was roped in and I was two hours from ABC. If I couldn't find the rope to Camp One, I'd just go back down. Ivan would shake his head and there'd be some perfectly reasonable explanation for why I'd missed the route. Maybe a small slide buried the fixed lines, or Ang had to take down the rope temporarily.

I crossed the rock ledge and proceeded to traverse the slope. My heart hammered in my chest. I had to stop part-way to let my pulse slow. The sun was still shining. It was still a beautiful day on the mountain. Only now I was scared. I pulled a one-litre Nalgene bottle from my small pack and sucked back half its contents. If only my confidence could be replenished so easily.

Be flexible, I said to myself – I talk to myself sometimes – and keep moving. I raised my knee until the snow was light enough to stretch my boot forward. Then I leaned forward at the hips and reached with my ice axe to help pull me across the deep pack. I repeated the process a dozen times, then started counting from one again. Finally I reached the point where I'd clipped into the horizontal traverse.

There was still no rope leading uphill to Camp One.

And now there was no fixed rope headed downhill either.

I framed my eyes with my hands and peered intently at the snow just five feet from me, the snow where I knew a stake had been buried, securing the end of a rope. There was no stake. There was no sign of footprints.

There was no rope, no sign of passage by anyone.

I kind of lost it at that point. That painting The Scream, by Edvard Munch? I'm pretty sure that was the expression on my face. No actual sound came out of my mouth, though.

I felt hunted, somehow, like I was a fawn hiding from a grizzly. Death could find me here. I was in the wrong place – I didn't know how or why – and I suddenly had no confidence that heading downhill would take me to the glacier or even any location on planet Earth.

Ivan found me. At first I thought he was a yeti, an abominable snowman come to devour me head-first. A man-shaped figure ducked and bobbed its way through a cluster of boulders scattered just above me. Ivan emerged from cover and I wondered how I hadn't recognized his bright green jacket.

"Don't move," he called out.

The head guide was still fifty feet away. I could see that a rope extended back from his harness to the boulders, and he had a loop of rope in his right hand.

"Don't move," he repeated.

I looked around, expecting to see a nest of rattlesnakes or a tiger twitching its tail. I saw no obvious threat.

Ivan crept towards me like a bomb technician approaching a suspicious package. When he was twenty feet away he stopped.

"I'm going to throw this line to you. I want you to clip into the figure eight tied at the end."

"Okay," I said. "Do you want me to unclip from the fixed line, too?"

He didn't answer. Maybe he didn't hear me. He swung his arm underhand, launching the coil of rope so it landed beyond and above me, ensuring that as it slid downhill there was no way I could miss it.

I found the knot and clipped it into a carabiner, only now I couldn't feel my second carabiner, the one attaching me to the horizontal fixed line. I tried to push the folds of my Gore-tex shell out of the way to get an eye on it. I finally found the second carabiner. It was where it should be, clipped into the main loop of my harness, just below my navel.

It wasn't clipped on to any rope, however. A wash of cold sweat bathed my back.

How had I not clipped in to the fixed line?

"Start moving, Phil. Slowly, slowly," said Ivan. He was beckoning with his right hand.

I looked back where I'd just come from. I could see the deep pockets where I'd wallowed across the slope, but I couldn't see the fixed line. The red rope was gone.

It was gone where I stood, too. It had been right there, I'd been clipped into it. The end of the rope had been fixed to a snow picket not five feet from where I stood.

No rope going down the mountain, no rope going up, and now no rope going across.

"Gotta move, Phil," said Ivan.

"I don't understand," I said.

"I know. Just come towards me."

The snow was even deeper than I thought. I had to use my arms to swim in the guide's direction.

"Not so hard, Phil. Gentle, gentle. And slow," he said.

It took me five minutes to cover the twenty feet separating us.

"The ropes are gone," I said when I reached him.

"I know. They're back this way. We're gonna go together."

Another five minutes took us to the boulders. Ivan stopped.

"What happened, Phil?" he asked.

I was looking at him, my mouth agape. I looked back where we'd just come from, then back at him.

"There was no rope going up. There was a rope going that way," I pointed.

"You almost walked into an avalanche," he said. "You couldn't see the snow load on that slope? It's a miracle it didn't let go."

"But that's where the rope went," I said.

Ivan shook his head.

"Do you see a rope, Phil? There's no rope."

Ivan forced me to finish the water in my Nalgene and he inspected my helmet to make sure nothing had hit me in the head. Then he short-roped me for ten minutes, just three metres separating us on the line. We crossed a narrow, icy couloir and slipped across a steep slope of dark grey scree. We were back on snow when I saw the bright red of the fixed lines. They cut across our traversing path, heading up and down the mountain. Ivan walked us up to the rope and clipped me onto it before detaching the short rope connecting us.

Later that night, tucked into my sleeping bag in Camp One, I struggled to fall asleep, the day's near-disaster looping in my head. I'd almost died and the reason was obvious. My mind was slipping. My brain couldn't be trusted. I was seeing things, imagining ropes where there were none, and missing ropes that *were* there.

I prayed silently to myself, to the mountain, to the void. Just hold on a little bit longer.

CHAPTER TWO

MAY 29

THE NEUROLOGIST SUGGESTED I think of fruit.

"It's about the size of a kiwi," she said, then turned her computer monitor to give me a view of the tumour in my brain.

I'd been having small symptoms for months when my family doc finally suggested sending me to a specialist. I was losing vocabulary and becoming irritated for no reason. Hardly neon signs. But then there was the day I lost vision in my left eye for an hour, and the time I blanked out in the grocery store. My GP thought it might be multiple sclerosis. Alzheimer's also runs in the family.

"You told me not to sugarcoat it," said the specialist, "so I won't. This is bad news. If it's glioblastoma, you need to get your affairs in order right now. If it's not, the location – this is your neocortex right here – still means operating is not an option. We'll get you on a course of chemo as soon as possible. With your tumour, I can fast-track it, so you'll probably start in about six to eight weeks..."

"Eight weeks?" I couldn't believe it. "How about right now?"

"I'm sorry. The delay won't make a large difference to your prognosis, if that's any comfort."

I grimaced: "That depends on the prognosis."

The doctor sat back in her chair. I liked her face. It was severe, a gaunt skull with close-cropped grey hair. Terrible with the whole bedside manner, of course, but I didn't need someone nice, I needed someone smart. Dr. Grable was chief of neurosurgery at the university hospital.

"It's not good, Mr. Truss. You may want a second opinion, someone more optimistic than me, but I've never seen a good outcome from a mass this size in this location. You might have a year. You might have considerably less."

"Jesus," I said.

Her mouth widened into a humourless grin.

"Praying may be your best bet," she said.

I left the appointment dazed. Cancer was not part of my plan. I was rich and single. I was supposed to have at least another two decades, maybe three or four. Many years enjoying my place at the top of the global pecking order.

I never worked hard at a career and I'm not especially smart. I did, however, buy the cryptocurrency Tulip. My father and I didn't get along. I hadn't seen him in five years when he died of Alzheimer's. I expected nothing from his estate. When I received two thousand dollars, I didn't know what to do with it. The money sat in a bank account until I saw a story on CBC about Tulip reaching parity with the US dollar. It seemed like an appropriately senseless way to spend the cash.

I got out late, after the crash. It cost me. But I still ended up with a little more than fourteen million.

I could have taken some of that dough and headed south of the border. Americans with money don't wait eight weeks for chemotherapy. I couldn't face being sick, though, not with so little hope it would make a difference. My body felt fit, the best I'd felt in years.

I was in training, actually, the summit of Mount Rainier in my sights.

Climbing mountains was born out of a conversation with Karen a couple of years prior. We married and divorced in our early twenties but remained friends. Just too young. I messed around, she wanted to mess around, so we ended it after a year.

When I got my Tulip windfall, I gave her a million just because she was the only person in the world who meant anything to me. Her husband was pissed.

We were out for lunch – her and I, definitely not him – and Karen asked what I was going to do with the money. I was reading *Into Thin Air* again, the Krakauer book about the 1996 Everest disaster. I told her I didn't know but that if I were to live my life over, I'd be a mountaineer.

"No second chances, Phil. You should do it. The biggest hurdle is the expense and you've got that one covered. I loved my trip, you know that."

Karen spent the summer after high school in Grindelwald, Switzerland. She scrambled up a few small peaks and even summited the Eiger, albeit not via the notorious north face.

I laughed at her suggestion: "The biggest hurdle is that I'm a middle-aged chickenshit with a fat gut and a bum knee."

She dismissed that with a wave of her hand.

"Lose twenty pounds and the knee will improve. I can't help you with the chickenshit part, though."

It was a ridiculous idea. I didn't like camping or the outdoors. Walking was dull. Snow or rain were to be avoided at all costs. It did get me thinking, though.

I'd turned fifty the previous year but looked older. I felt ugly. Women were attracted to my money, sure, but paunchy and pale wasn't turning any heads. I felt shitty, too. I'd wake in the middle of the night gasping for air. Getting in and out of my low-slung Nissan left me out of breath.

Change began with a short walk. Ten minutes to the store and ten minutes back. I was moving.

I added a few minutes each day. Once a week I drove out of the city for a short hike. I started eating better, too. No calorie counting – that was hard even in my twenties – but I started cutting categories of food out of my diet. First it was sweets, then bread. Cheese got the axe and so did pasta. I went vegetarian to curb my cravings for bologna (thick cut and fried, with honey mustard) and started buying myself a single four-pack of beer to last the week.

The weight dropped. The knee felt better. I was lighter and getting stronger.

Three months after the conversation with Karen, I booked a one-week beginner mountaineering course for the subsequent summer. I trained through the winter. Every Sunday I drove to Ski Martock to walk up and down their six hundred-foot hill. When a blizzard shut down Halifax in the first week of February, I walked the streets for five hours, ending my odyssey on Citadel Hill. Just me and a few tobogganers.

I flew out to Calgary on June 1st. Four days later I stood atop a small peak called Mount Olive, five thousand feet above Bow Lake. Snow-capped summits filled the horizon in every direction. The vast whiteness of the Wapta icefield stretched out below us.

The week was spent exploring the glacier and traipsing up and down low mountains. Evenings found us hunkered in the warmth of the Bow Hut kitchen, trading stories, dealing cards, and making friends like we were teenagers again. It was great.

During the two-hour van ride back to the guiding company's headquarters in Canmore I was already thinking about my next objective. By the time I reached the Calgary airport, I'd settled on Mount Rainier. It was big and tall, looming more than 14,000 feet above Seattle, and a suitable next step towards, well, I wasn't sure. Canada's tallest mountain, Logan? Clambering up the Matterhorn in Switzerland? Some day risking life and limb in the Khumbu Icefall?

I was four months from my trip to Rainier when Dr. Grable told me about the kiwi.

Chapter Three

July 13

AFTER MY SOLO misadventure Ivan insisted I go back down the mountain to Base Camp. "You're seeing a neurologist," he said. We were just out of the icefall en route to Base from ABC.

"I don't think there's a neurologist this side of Islamabad," I said.

"He's flying in. Be here this afternoon."

A two million-dollar expedition budget affords one certain privileges. Apparently that included having a neurologist on-call.

As we walked by the tents of the other teams, I caught a few wary glances. Had word already spread about the incident? Climbers worry when other climbers don't have their shit together. An unfit climber is, at best, a serious nuisance, for example needing a rescue that could derail a summit attempt. At worst, they're a lethal hazard, for example triggering an avalanche that could derail continuing to live.

I gave a nod to those who kept eye contact long enough. When we reached the two hundred-yard gap between the Italian tents and ours, I complained to Ivan.

"Jesus, it's not like somebody died."

He looked around, like maybe someone was eavesdropping from behind a pile of gravel.

"Actually, someone did, this morning. One of Spain's. Pulmonary edema. They waited too long to call in the rescue. They're on a shoestring, so they didn't have insurance for air rescue, and hesitated about paying the whole shot."

Teams bought insurance. Pay Pakistan's air force whatever the amount was in advance – thousands of dollars – and if you needed an air rescue, you got one.

"I thought it was mandatory," I said.

He shook his head.

"Used to be. But with fewer requests for permits because of the war, they've eased the regs. Besides, nobody's worried about climbers killing themselves on mountains when hometown boys are getting blown up by IEDs two valleys over. Dying on K2 is elitist, don't you know, so fuck the rich foreigners."

My doctor arrived just before supper. You could hear the chopper before you could pick it out from the backdrop of peaks. It was just a pinpoint when I finally spotted it, but it grew quickly. The helicopter covered the distance from Concordia in minutes. To my surprise it wasn't painted in the livery of the air force. The sleek machine looked like something you'd expect to see landing on top of a skyscraper in Manhattan.

Ivan and I stood hunched at the edge of the landing zone our camp manager Raymond had marked with a spray-painted X.

"Sorry!" Ivan shouted to me. "The army was using its helos today, so other arrangements were made."

I cringed at the optics. The timing couldn't have been worse. I imagined every person at the Spanish camp glaring in our direction. At least it was a doctor being flown in, not a cooler of Cristal, poached lobster and foie gras.

Dr. Abbas was younger than I expected. Late thirties, trim, dressed like a gentleman hiker in brand-spanking-new Arcteryx and Patagonia. He also had a face mask on, with a bottle of O's in a slim pack on his back. We shook hands but waited until we'd walked back to our kitchen tent to start speaking.

We sat down with mugs of tea. I described my solo attempt to reach Camp One and Ivan explained how he'd found me. Abbas had me perform a number of physical tests, none of them strenuous. I had to do deep knee bends without holding on to a support for balance. He made me stand tall and tip my head back with my eyes closed. Then I had to alternately reach in with my index fingers and touch my nose. He got me to strip down to a tee-shirt and ran a pen down the length of my arm, asking me to describe the sensation ("Ticklish"), and told me to hold my hands out in front of me and then pulled down on each as I tried to resist.

He peered into my eyes next and used a handheld light to watch my pupils as I looked in different directions. His respiration was loud in the plastic mask covering his mouth and nose. Base camp is above 16,000 feet. Without oxygen, he risked passing out or worse.

Finally, the doctor listened to my chest with a stethoscope and took my blood pressure.

I wondered if he would dismiss us for a few minutes while he tabulated my results but apparently that wasn't necessary. It struck me that what I'd been given wasn't too different from a field sobriety test: the maneuvers cops make suspected drunk drivers perform at the side of the road.

"It's not HACE," Abbas said. "Probably."

"Probably," said Ivan.

"Impossible to rule out, but I don't see any physical sign of cerebral edema," said the doctor. "How aggressive are your rotations?"

Rotations. He was asking Ivan about our climbing schedule. Getting to the top of a mountain as tall as K2 can't be done in a single push. The body needs to adapt to changes in elevation. The standard phrase is "climb high, sleep low." Go a little ways up the mountain, then come back down. The next trip, go a bit higher. The body adapts to lower air pressure and reduced oxygen. Edema can happen even with a conservative plan, but climb too high too fast and you were inviting altitude sickness.

"We're taking it slow," said Ivan.

The doctor nodded. "Well, I think the most likely culprit is the tumour. I spoke with your doctor in America…"

"Canada," I said.

"…and confusion, even hallucinations, are consistent with your diagnosis."

I asked if it could happen again.

"Oh, undoubtedly, and probably with more frequency. As a physician, I feel duty-bound to tell you that K2 is the last place on Earth you should be right now, but I could say the same thing if you didn't have a brain tumour, yes?"

He smiled at his joke.

CHAPTER FOUR

MAY 29

I CALLED KAREN after my neurologist in Halifax diagnosed the tumour.

"What are you going to do?" she asked.

"I suppose I'm gonna die," I said.

I'd asked the specialist if I could still climb Rainier.

"You can until you can't," the doc had said. "When your body says you can do something, do it. You may not have another chance. And don't wait four months."

My ex invited me out to the south shore for a couple of days.

"Bobby's in Boston for work, but he won't mind."

He probably didn't. Karen and I stopped having flings years before she met him. It was just too confusing. I still loved curling up on a couch with her for a movie marathon, though.

"What are we watching?" I asked. They had a big home just outside Chester, an hour from the city. The view of the ocean was spectacular. Was it weird that I found their place so restful?

"Rogue One," she called from the kitchen.

She was a Star Wars fiend. We'd already seen this one, opening night at the theatre. It was okay, but I was an Empire Strikes Back man, myself. Not because I was a "hopeless romantic," as Karen claimed. I just liked Boba Fett.

We hadn't talked about cancer or my imminent departure, not for Rainier – I'd changed my booking so I could fly out the following week – or from life.

The best part of Rogue One was the scene at the end when Darth Vader was murdering rebels in pursuit of the Death Star plans. The second-best part of the movie was the black battle droid, K2-SO. That robot had great one-liners.

Three-quarters of the way through the film, K2-SO was at a control panel helping the humans find a computer file – it's a little more entertaining than it sounds – when he was interrupted by stormtroopers. A firefight ensued and the battlebot was killed. I started weeping.

"Everyone dies in this stupid movie," I sobbed.

"I know," said Karen. She started wailing, too.

I spluttered out a choked laugh. We were crying and hugging when my diseased brain made the connection.

The robot.

K2-SO.

"Why am I climbing Rainier?" I said.

Karen pulled back. Her eyes were puffy, her face mottled red. She looked very pretty. I wanted to kiss her cheeks but I didn't.

"What are you talking about?" she said.

"Rainier. Why am I climbing it? Karen, fuck that little mountain. Think about it. What's the thing that stops people from swimming with great white sharks or base jumping off the CN Tower?"

I was on my feet. Karen was looking up at me, bewildered.

"A desire not to be an idiot?" she guessed.

I smiled. I felt giddy, maybe a bit unhinged.

"Yes, a desire not to be an idiot. Definitely. But also fear. Fear of dying. And what's the last thing I need to worry about now? Dying. I should be skydiving, Karen. I should be mainlining heroin or putting on a Batman costume and fighting crime. Don't you see? I've got nothing to lose. I should be taking chances.

"I shouldn't be climbing Rainier. I should be climbing K2."

Blame a photo for my interest in the world's second tallest peak. Krakauer's bestseller wasn't the only mountaineering tome on my bookshelf. Everest is taller and Annapurna has a higher fatality rate, but after I saw a black and white picture of K2's east face taken during the 1909 expedition I was smitten.

The first ridgeline in the foreground is a vertical rock face thousands of feet high. Behind it soars another wall atop of which is a swollen glacier large enough to cover five peaks in the Rockies. And then, still further, and so much higher, the summit pyramid, next to which the wonders of Egypt – the wonders of humanity – are mere pebbles.

It's a vast, alien sentinel; an observer measuring time in eons. Impenetrable. Deadly and wondrous. It's hard to fathom life existing even for a moment in that high place.

The raw statistics are unnerving. The ratio of successful summits to deaths is four-to-one. The average slope incline exceeds 55 degrees. The summit is more than 28,000 feet above sea level and the elevation change from Base Camp to the top is 13,000 vertical feet.

It's very cold as well. The whole region is hammered with storms year-round and a K2 climber should expect to spend their summer battling howling blizzards and temperatures that send Siberians indoors. Even when you catch a warm day – and they do happen, ideally when you're in Camp Four hoping to summit – it's a mixed blessing: you're less likely to freeze your nose off but more likely to be crushed by a rock that's wiggled loose in the thaw.

Its climbing history is suitably grandiose. K2's biography is replete with scandals and tragedies, epic feats and survival stories. The wealthy and famous are amongst its earliest explorers, including an Italian duke and Aleister Crowley, an occult figure best known for being branded "the wickedest man in the world" by a British newspaper.

It's K2's appearance, though, that captured my imagination. Everest hides in its own massif, guarded by the walls of sister peaks Nuptse and Lhotse, while Annapurna is a long ridgeline of competing peaks. K2 is alone. It waits at the end of the Baltoro Glacier. The planet's largest solitary monument.

A grand memorial.

CHAPTER FIVE

JULY 14

WE WERE UP early the morning after the doctor's Base Camp house-call. Ivan wanted to take advantage of clear weather to push up to Camp Two. So far heights and exposure hadn't been a major psychological factor. I suspected House's Chimney might change that.

The chimney is the toughest thirty metres on K2. Sure, the Black Pyramid section – a thousand feet of near-vertical climbing – is far longer and more dangerous. Summit day, with the Bottleneck, seracs and traverse, claims the most victims. But the chimney, first climbed in 1938 by Bill House, requires the most technical climbing. It's a narrow, vertical half-pipe in a cliff face lying just below Camp Two.

House soloed it back in the era of hobnailed boots and tweed climbing blazers. We would be climbing it with the security of a wire ladder, as well as fixed ropes.

My stomach was in knots as we ate muesli and powdered milk for breakfast. Almost everyone has a fear of heights. The real question is how extreme the circumstances need to be before it kicks in. Most people can bring themselves to walk across the glass floor in the CN Tower's main pod, a hundred stories above the ground, but almost everyone would balk at perching on a one-foot square platform on the pinpoint top of that same building.

Exposure is a hard thing to quantify. The north face of the Eiger is vastly more difficult than the Matterhorn. Yet when I watch footage of both climbs, the latter looks more intimidating. The Eiger is a wide wall, whereas the route up the Matterhorn follows an extremely steep ridgeline to the summit. In the first case, terror lurks beneath your feet, but in the second the world falls away on both sides, *as well as* beneath you.

So which route is more dangerous? The Eiger, no debate. Which one looks more exposed when I watch it on film? Definitely the Matterhorn.

The chimney is only a hundred feet but it's a hundred feet piled atop steep slopes thousands of feet tall. The view would drop straight down to the glacier below.

Ivan gave me his version of a pep talk as we walked through Base Camp.

"This is going to push your fitness. You'll be amazed at how tiring it is, even with the ladder. Your toughest day so far, but you'll do it. You're starting to make me a believer, Phil. I didn't think you'd make it to Base Camp. No, really. And now you're a day's climb from Camp Two on K2. You heard the doc: you're in great shape for a man who's dying."

One of the Koreans called out to us from their mess tent as we passed. We stopped as he jogged over.

"Come tent. You want see," said the man. I couldn't remember his name although I recognized him from a meal we'd shared. I'd always been useless with names. Brain cancer hadn't helped.

Smiles greeted us from the dining table. The sizeable crowd at breakfast was less than half their total number. A woman rose with a shy grin and beckoned to me. I smiled back. We followed her around a second table to a small bench where three laptops were open. She squatted down at the first one and used the touch pad below the keyboard to open a webpage. She looked up at me.

"This you, yes?"

The page she'd opened was a climbing portal. The headline filled the upper quarter of the screen: 'K2 for Sale.' Below it, the subhead read 'Dying Canadian buys way up mountain.'

Ouch.

I didn't linger over the words. I felt too self-conscious standing in a tent full of my peers reading a story pointing out that I wasn't, in fact, one of their peers. Could bringing this story to my attention be some kind of passive-aggressive reprimand from the Korean team? Did this story represent the general sentiment of Base Camp?

None of the teams were quoted in the piece, although the tip-off probably came from camp. There was a ten-second video clip of the previous day's helicopter arrival. You could just make me out as a bright blue spot, waiting, buffeted by rotor wash.

The perspective encapsulated in the story was nothing new. There's a particular strain of expert climber who despises anyone who doesn't practice their form of mountaineering. You climbed like them – no sherpas, no porters, no oxygen or fixed lines – or you were an imposter. What I was doing wasn't just breaking their rules, it was blasphemy. The author of the article came right out and said it: "One might as well install an elevator up the Abruzzi."

The criticism wasn't without merit. There is a profound difference between being guided up a mountain that's been fixed the whole way with ropes, and venturing out by yourself or with a few companions to put up a new route on a lethal peak. But an elevator?

21

The word multi-millionaire appeared at least six times in the short piece. I wasn't a climber, according to the editorialist, I was a wealthy tourist. It felt like the writer had real hatred for me. That impression was reinforced by the last sentence: "I hate this man and everything he represents. He doesn't deserve to be buried on K2."

Ivan finished reading the clip.

"Wow," he said.

Wow indeed.

Chapter Six

June 2

IVAN WOULDN'T EVEN meet me at first.

I got no response to my email or Facebook messages, not even after I played the cancer card. There was no reply to the attempts I made through his sponsors. I finally left a voice message with his guiding company offering him ten grand to meet me for lunch: half an hour and I'd never bother him again.

Lunch for him but a weekend for me. His office was in Chamonix, France. A long way to go just to offer someone a job. But I knew he was the right guy for the gig.

I flew to Paris, connected to Geneva, Switzerland, then caught a helicopter over the border into the valley. The view was incredible. I tried to imagine K2's Karakoram range, mountains double the size of the Alps.

The limo drove me to a small hotel. It was an unremarkable room and cost a fortune but I had a private bath. I cleaned off the muck of travel in the shower then dressed quickly. I made it to the restaurant ten minutes before our agreed time. Ivan was already there, waiting in the foyer.

"Do you have my ten thousand?" were his first words.

I handed over a thick envelope stuffed with euros.

"I almost didn't come," he said once we were seated. "Thought this was a hoax."

His refusal came as soon as the waiter finished taking our drink order.

"It's a ridiculous idea. You're not a climber. Find a teenager to pull you up Mont Blanc."

The Ukrainian's accent was very faint. He'd spent his late teens and twenties climbing in the States.

"I don't want to climb Mont Blanc," I said. "I want to climb K2."

He swished a mouthful of water like he was rinsing a foul taste from his palate.

"This is a little offensive, you understand?" he said. "Like telling David Beckham you play soccer with your mates and now you want to be in the World Cup. It's beyond arrogant to think you can do what I do."

I had no expectations of climbing like Ivan.

Ivan Honcharuk should have won the Platina Cepin. It's an award the mountaineering community bestows on its most skilled and ambitious members. Nominations are picked by a committee. The list of winners is a who's-who of the sport, from Sir Edmund Hillary to Anatoli Boukreev. These are the giants of climbing and alpinism. Ivan should be among them.

Two years before we met in Chamonix he put up a route on K2 so audacious the committee balked at even granting a nomination. They were upfront about their reasoning: they feared setting a suicidal standard for future aspirants. The quote by the group's president, reported by the world's press, summed up their position: "This is not climbing. This is Russian roulette."

Ivan's reckless accomplishment was free soloing the massive ice face above K2's Bottleneck. It's a notoriously unstable glacial wall eight kilometres above sea level. He used an ice tool in each hand and crampons on his boots. He didn't place a single piece of protective gear or touch a rope.

It was bonkers, plain and simple. He climbed it in three hours, then capped the accomplishment by continuing to the summit, oxygen-free, and bivouacking there overnight. His reward was losing two toes and a finger to frostbite. No Platina Cepin.

If anyone could get a rookie to the top it was him.

"That's not it. I don't think I can do what you do," I said. "I believe you're so good that even doing something as ridiculous as taking a complete novice to the summit of the second highest mountain on Earth is within your power. My guess is you could drag a family of four to the top of Everest, throw in grandpa for good measure."

I had one opportunity to get him onboard and I'd traveled a long way to do it. The waiter brought wine while I waited for his reply. Ivan drank half a glass before he spoke.

"Well, what about Everest?" he finally said. "Less technical, easier to support, more options if we have to bail."

I shook my head.

"I'm not bailing. I'll summit or die trying. K2 will be my tombstone. No, it's got to be this mountain."

The food arrived. Ivan didn't touch it. He frowned.

"There are vertical sections, ice and rock. Can you even climb?"

I could climb some. I'd been visiting a gym every week since my trip to Olive. It was a loaded question, though, like being asked by Floyd Mayweather if I knew how to counterpunch.

"Only a little," I said. "I climb five-nine indoors."

"Indoors," he nodded. Then he shook his head and smiled, clearly entertained by the absurdity of the situation.

"Listen, I'm in decent shape. The fittest I've ever been," I continued. "I'm not sick, not yet. There's a little ski hill where I live, six hundred vertical feet. Last week I went up and down it eight times with a fifty-pound—."

"So five thousand feet at sea level," he interrupted, "and indoor climbing five-nine? Look, despite what you may have heard, I'm not crazy. You might find someone to take you up this hill, but it won't be me. I'd be a joke, you'd be dead and—"

It was my turn to interrupt: "I'm going to be dead regardless."

He stopped. It might have been sympathy I saw on his face.

"I'm sorry. It's not for me. I have to go."

I stood as he stood. I'd saved the best for last.

"You haven't asked me what the job pays," I said.

He reached over the table and picked up the half-empty bottle of wine.

"I have all the money I need," he said. "I don't need yours."

"One million dollars," I said.

He raised the bottle and drank from it, then ran the back of his hand across his mouth.

"No," he said.

"Two. Two million dollars."

He started to turn away.

"Six million."

I said this loud enough to stop the other conversations in the small restaurant.

"Six million for you. That's just your fee. I have another two million to pay for the expedition. And you don't even have to bring me back alive. Easiest fortune you'll ever make."

He stood with his back to me and raised the bottle of red wine for a long pull. I just caught his voice as he walked away.

"Nothing about this will be easy."

25

CHAPTER SEVEN

JULY 15

"BIG DAY TODAY," said Ivan as he licked his spoon clean of instant oatmeal.

We'd spent the night at Camp One. I'd slept poorly, bad dreams I couldn't remember. Fear gripped my guts as an imaginary clock ticked down to our departure from the relative safety of the tent. Ivan clipped me onto a short rope before we even left the shelter. We wouldn't be using the fixed line. It allowed for rapid descents but Ivan felt it slowed us going uphill.

After I clumsily attached my crampons outside, he bent over to double-check the fit.

"It's all in the details," he said. "Get the details right – pay attention to the little stuff – and good things happen on the mountain. Sloppy gets you dead."

It was a familiar message. Ivan would get indignant when he saw a backpack with loose objects hung on loops with carabiners. Each time we left the tent he asked if I knew the contents of my pack. With my ailing memory, I had a checklist I had to show him, marks in pencil proving I had completed the ritual. "Be squared away or be left behind," he said one time. It had the ring of a mantra. I suspect the slogan went beyond its literal meaning with him. Ivan could slot actions, people, everything in the world into those two categories.

I fit both categories: squared away until it was time to be left behind.

Ang didn't wait for us. He was fast. Ivan told me Ang once nabbed the summit of Everest from Camp Two in the Western Cwm and made it back down to the South Col before dark. Ivan sent his colleague ahead to make sure the trail was well-broken to the chimney, the crux of the day's climb.

I started feeling better once we were moving. Every morning my lower back and thighs screamed at me but half an hour into climbing they'd warm up and stop protesting. The route was steep without pause. I kept my steps short. Sometimes I turned my toes out to minimize the involvement of my calf muscles – they tire more quickly than the leg's larger muscle groups and I needed to save them to front-point the chimney – but much of the time I was sidestepping.

I used my ice axe, planting the pointed bottom of the shaft a couple of feet uphill and hauling with my arm. I had a merde grip, a derisive term because it's the way you hold the tool if you anticipate needing to self-arrest. The adze faces forward and the pick backwards so that, if you fall, the sharp point of the pick can be turned

26

immediately into the slope. It was the way I was taught in Canada and Ivan saw no reason to change it.

I didn't use an ice axe leash. I brought a wrist leash to Pakistan but Ivan discouraged its use.

"Slows you down. The axe needs to change to your uphill hand frequently, and speed is safety."

"What if I drop my axe?" I'd asked.

"Don't."

We paused after an hour and a half for a water break. I kept a one-litre bottle in a pocket on my climbing bag but it was a pain to reach while underway. I wasn't usually thirsty anyway. I had to force myself to down cups of water in the tent at the end of the day.

"Almost there," said Ivan.

A surge of fear stiffened my back. I asked the question I'd resisted asking.

"How hard is it compared to the other stuff we've done?"

"Toughest section on the route," he said, "but you'll be clipped in the whole time. Just don't give up on me. You'll get through it."

So it would be agony.

Being at your work-output limit for an extended period of time is uniquely miserable. Boxers risk getting punched in the face rather than using exhausted shoulders to keep their hands up. Look at wildlife documentaries: eventually the bison tires and stops fighting the wolves.

In the case of animals, though, maybe their willpower hasn't abandoned them, maybe the tank is just empty. Humans are almost never put in a situation where they truly empty the tank. We give up because we give up.

We passed around a rock outcropping and got our first glimpse of the wall.

"Over there," said Ivan.

The snow was blowing pretty hard. I couldn't see what he was pointing at. We trudged up to the foot of the cliff and traversed left. The chimney appeared in front of us when we were right on top of it.

Jesus. It looked like some great claw gouged a trough out of the vertical face. The chimney wasn't as sheltered as I'd imagined it would be; it was shallower, more exposed. At least visibility wasn't great. When I climbed the chimney and looked down I'd only see a few hundred feet of imminent death, instead of thousands.

"Take a break, Phil. Not too long, though," said Ivan.

I didn't want to take a break. I feared what my mind would do if I waited. I hadn't realized I could still be so terrified by heights. I did need to catch my breath, though.

"Okay," I said.

I felt like I was going to piss my pants. I took a drink of water anyway. The chute didn't look very technical. Lots of exposed handholds. And there was a wire ladder. I couldn't see much beyond a bump thirty feet up, where the angle steepened – hopefully briefly – beyond 90 degrees.

I glanced back the way we'd come.

We can go back down. I don't have to do this.

I let the thought tickle my brain: I was going to die – not from a tumour, not from some half-imagined future disaster – I was going to die today. I'd climb this thing and slip and fall. I'd get halfway up and have a heart attack.

This is too hard. Why am I doing this to myself?

I was on the verge of panic. I looked back up the route. The overhanging section would be short. It had to be. Then it would be just like the climbing gym, but colder. And wearing a snowsuit and heavy boots. With half the oxygen I was used to.

Ivan patted me on the shoulder.

"Climb this," he said, "and you'll know you can climb the toughest hundred feet this mountain has to offer."

I stepped up to the bottom of the chimney. My heart rate was already near max just from nerves. It boggled my mind that a man made the first ascent of this treacherous feature without fixed ropes or ladders. I wondered if our sherpas had to free-climb it or if the fixed lines and ladder were leftovers from a previous season.

You could tell some of the ropes were very old. Frayed tat blossomed from old pitons like strange polyester flowers. Ivan clipped my ascender onto our fixed rope. I quashed the thought that a single rope was what stood between me and death. I concentrated instead on using the flimsy wire ladder.

The word 'ladder' sounds reassuring, but each rung was barely wide enough for a boot. I couldn't climb it. It served, instead, as a wobbly point from which I could gain other holds. I kept my left hand on the ladder and used my right hand to fumble for grips. My left foot was usually on a rung. I kicked my right boot into the hard ice that covered most of the granite.

I barely looked up. I avoided looking down. The whole world was contained in the length of my heaving body. I was absolutely exhausted by the time I reached the overhang thirty feet from where I started. I wanted to slump on my harness and catch my breath. As soon as I stopped moving upwards, though, Ivan started shouting at me.

"No! No, no! Don't rest. Keep going."

I felt the ladder twist in the grip of my left hand. I looked down. Ivan was starting up the route. Maybe he'd walk me up the whole chimney, take me safely to the top.

He reached me in less than a minute and then kept climbing. For a brief moment, as he passed, his suited bulk hemmed me in, kept the void at bay. If only we could climb all of K2 that way. If only Ivan was twelve feet tall and could wear me in an oversized Baby Bjorn.

I caught his voice as he passed from view over the hump.

"...on your own. You need to prove this to yourself."

Goddamn you, Ivan, and your Tony Robbins bullshit.

A wave of self-pity threatened to paralyze me. I could be home, warm and safe, and not fearing for my life. But then I remembered why I was there. My life wasn't in danger, my life was forfeit. Death was coming for me no matter what. I was just meeting it on my own terms.

CHAPTER EIGHT

JUNE 9

I RETURNED TO Halifax after enlisting Ivan. I spent a lot of time with Karen in the final two weeks before departure. Her husband was always with us. I didn't know whether that was his plan or Karen's.

There was a fantasy in my mind that she and I would sleep together a final time. Robert would have her for the rest of his life. She was mine first and I'd be dead. It felt like I should get to have that. That's not how it worked out.

Farewell was a series of conversations that never felt as genuine as they should have; gestures of physical affection that were awkward, even embarrassing. She helped me shop for gear and accompanied me to the clinic for vaccinations. Robert came along, too. He usually waited in the car, his face buried in his cellphone. It was clad in plastic armour he took immense pride in bragging about.

"Cost me two-twenty-five. Usually four hundred, but I know the distributor. Waterproof to six hundred metres. This case can take a direct shot from an AR-15."

Unlikely in Halifax. I wanted to ding it off his face.

The day I was flying out I'd finally had enough. Karen came to the airport to say good-bye and this time Robert came inside, like he needed to monitor my final opportunity to grope his wife.

I was going to let it go. I was going to shake hands with him and give Karen a chaste little hug, and then get in line for security and not look back. I was surprised by a wave of emotion and found myself choking back tears. I felt angry and embarrassed. Karen overheard me swearing under my breath and asked what was wrong.

"This! This is wrong," I said. "Rob being a vulture, you and me doing this 'nice to know ya' routine. It's all bullshit. It's not the way it's supposed to be."

Robert looked like he was going to say something but thankfully Karen spoke first.

"You don't have to go," she said. "I don't want you to go. You should be at home with us."

"You and 'Bobby.' Yeah, that's just great," I grumbled.

"With me, with the people who love you…" Her voice trailed off. I was already shaking my head.

"Policeman Bobby," I said.

"That's not fair," said Karen.

Then Robert surprised me.

"It's not like that," he said. "Babe, I'm gonna go wait in the car. And Phil, I hope you reach the top of the mountain. I really do. You're important to Karen and that makes you important to me. I wish you happiness, brother."

Karen waited until her husband was out of earshot.

"He's a good man," she said.

I nodded. "He better be. 'Brother'?"

"Oh stop. He *is* a good man. And he feels bad about what's happened. I think he always hoped the two of you would be closer."

"That's just weird," I said.

"I don't know what's weird anymore," said Karen. "You're killing yourself on K2. Not quite as outrageous as being shot out of a cannon like Hunter Thompson, but still, drama much?"

I smiled. Tears flowed down my cheeks. Karen hugged me then, tight, and she kissed each of my cheeks. Then she kissed me on the mouth. I held her and she mashed her lips against mine, both her hands pulling my head to her.

"I love you, Phil. I always will," she said when we separated.

"You're the only person I ever loved," I answered. "I just wish I'd been better."

She shook her head but didn't speak. I held her hand until she pulled her fingers loose. She turned and walked away and didn't look back.

Expeditions to K2 aren't typically planned in two weeks. The paperwork alone takes months to organize. Judicious use of cash by Ivan made bureaucratic wheels turn in record time. It helped that hostilities in Kashmir had escalated. Pakistan was hurting for climbers. Ivan had our permits with him when he met me at Islamabad International Airport.

"Are there usually tanks in the streets?" I asked.

Our taxi idled in a sea of trucks, cars and homemade vehicles (a donkey cart-motorcycle hybrid was a highlight). A mobile artillery piece was parked in the centre of the highway, sandbags stacked around it. Half a dozen soldiers smoked cigarettes in the shade of the armoured vehicle. Two of the soldiers were vigilant, however, parked behind a heavy machine gun trained on oncoming traffic, pointed at us.

"Everybody's jumpy," said Ivan. "We're leaving the city tomorrow, so it doesn't matter."

"No trouble?"

The Ukrainian shook his head.

31

"No one is climbing in the Karakoram, not with India and Pakistan trading punches. There're only five teams at Base Camp this season, including us. They still soaked us, though. Permits were triple the usual price by the time everyone got a taste. At least we won't have to put up with a government liaison eating our supplies at Base Camp. There're real things for soldiers to do these days."

We took a private flight to Skardu the next day. The town is a little over two hundred miles from Islamabad. The streets were nearly empty when we exited the small airport.

"This place should be hopping," said Ivan. "Expeditions buying supplies, porters looking for work, hotels sold out. It's never been like the Annapurna hiking circuit or Everest Base, but they did okay. It's dead now."

Our sirdar, the head climbing sherpa, was waiting for us in the lobby of a small guesthouse. Ang's shoulders were wide and so was his smile. He was a half-foot shorter than me, probably thirty pounds lighter – a small man, really – but he radiated vigor, like you'd recharge just standing next to him.

"I'm so pleased to meet you. And thank you, thank you so much," I said as we shook hands.

"Pleasure is mine," he answered. "We will have good climb, that is true."

"Congratulations," said Ivan.

"Thank you."

"Ang here has a new son," said Ivan to me.

"Oh wow. Congratulations," I said.

"His third," said Ivan.

"Sorry to take you away from the baby. Your wife can't be too happy about that," I said.

Ang stayed smiling. "I can do more for my family here than at home."

"Where are the boys?" Ivan asked his sirdar.

"Buying supplies," said Ang. His team of three sherpa guides were staying at the guesthouse as well. Porters and our basecamp manager would be waiting for us at the next stop.

Ivan placed his arm across the man's shoulders.

"Ang is one of the greatest alpinists alive today," he said, "just don't share a tent with him after eating cook's lentil curry."

Ang didn't miss a beat.

"You snore like a yak," said the smiling sherpa. "Probably from sexing them."

Ivan frowned. "I *am* quite fond of livestock," he said.

CHAPTER NINE

JULY 15

MY THROAT RATTLED as I gulped air. I took two big, chest-expanding lungfuls, then pushed myself up the chimney's overhang. My right foot scrambled for purchase. I moved my right hand to the ladder and used my arms to pull. I momentarily thought about trying to free my ice axe from its place strapped on my back but dismissed the idea. Pulling the axe off my pack on flat ground was tricky enough.

"Come on Phil, you wuss," I said aloud, "get up there."

I came over the top of the bulge. I looked up. No sign of Ivan. I couldn't see the top of the chimney. The snow was really driving and visibility couldn't have been more than ten metres or so. I rested on the ladder, my left arm hooked through a rung. I just needed my heart rate to come down a little

The thought occurred to me that there were no visual cues in sight that told me which way was up and which way was down. Strange thing to think but my brain latched on to it. The ladder looked the same both ways and so did the ropes. The exposed rocks and ice, too. Gravity was the only clue – a pretty solid indicator, granted, but in that moment it seemed like a thin hold on reality, a hold that could slip loose: What if I was actually climbing *down* the mountain to the summit? Or what if I was turned around and climbing back towards Camp One? Could the tumour mess up the way I sensed gravity?

Silly notions, but not in that moment. I really thought I might flip out and lose my mind.

Was that a voice I heard? It sounded familiar. I looked down past my feet and saw nothing. A white wall concealing a void that stretched clear down to the glacier. I looked the other way – up, just say it's up – and saw no sign of another person, just more rock and mist.

The sound came again, drifting down from above.

"I'm coming," I yelled back.

I had to move. What I didn't want was to be saved. Ivan was giving me a test and I was on the verge of failing.

I raised my right foot and kicked the toe spikes of the crampons into the ice. Gravel and snow cascaded down the chimney. I kicked again at the same spot, and then a third time before I found purchase. Then I pushed upward with my right thigh.

33

The feeling in my lungs, in my heart, was a constant assault on my willpower. My body begged to stop. How many rungs did I climb before my next rest? I tried to count but lost track shortly after ten.

"…keep pushing…"

The voice sounded intimate, right in my ear, but it was just an effect of the chimney, channeling sound down to me. I still couldn't see the top or my guide.

I wanted to weep. I wanted someone to take away the burden I had imposed on myself. I wanted to rid myself of the horrible knowledge that I would end.

I stopped moving. Took a breath and coughed. Took another breath. It was peaceful in the chimney when I wasn't trying to go anywhere. The wind was blocked and I was alone. I pressed my face into the snow.

The scrape of crampons beneath me. I looked down between my feet. A climber in the white, a grey shape drawing closer, clearer. It had to be Ang.

The sherpa was supposed to be up top, but we were the only team on the Abruzzi and he was the only climber besides Ivan and me at the chimney. It didn't matter why the plan had changed. I didn't want to be rescued – not physically carried – but the company of the sirdar would make all the difference. The tension in my stomach relaxed and I started making promises to myself that as soon as he reached me, I'd do my very best to push hard for the top.

"Phil."

Ivan's face looked down at me. I hadn't even noticed the steady trickle of ice and gravel he'd dislodged climbing down to meet me.

"What are you doing, bud?"

I blinked the snowflakes out of my eyelashes.

"Waiting for Ang," I said.

Ivan frowned.

"Ang is up top," he said. "He's waiting for you with a mug of hot tea."

It took all my energy just to lift my head and stare up the chimney at Ivan.

"He's just below. We're climbing together."

Ivan shuffled to one side so he could see past me.

"Nothing there, Phil," he said.

I looked down. The white curtain hid the foot of the funnel. There was no one.

"Maybe I fell asleep," I mumbled. "Dreaming – Ang – it was –"

"You gotta keep going, okay?" said Ivan. "I'll be right ahead of you."

He clambered up three rungs of the ladder and stopped. Just that short distance looked impossible. I didn't know I could feel so tired.

"Come on. You're doing good. It's almost over," he said.

I climbed. Ivan climbed. It seemed like hours before I caught a glimpse of the chimney's top. I recognized Ang's bright orange shell jacket. Wasn't that the same colour the climber beneath me was wearing? Now I wasn't so sure.

"Told you we were close," said Ivan. "You've done real good, Phil. Now let's finish strong."

I imagined I was a robot, an automaton forced to do the bidding of its human pilot: I require you to lift your left foot, I require you to reach with your right hand.

Somehow the pain became less vital. The screaming in my muscles muted a little. I imagined a place beyond pain. Then I wondered where you went if that place overflowed with pain, too. Maybe there was another escape. I hoped so. The idea that perceived limits are just obstacles we can bust through, over and over again forever, was very appealing.

Ivan was at the top. Only four rungs separated me from exiting the chimney. I could see Ang clearly. He was off to one side, making room for Ivan to scramble through but close enough to lend a hand. How did he get past me? How was he below me and above?

You're seeing things, Phil.

Two rungs left. The hardest part of K2 and I was almost done. My breath came in ragged gasps. My chest heaved trying to bring in enough oxygen. Ivan was gone but Ang waited. His hand stretched towards me. Safety.

I reached with my left hand and gripped Ang's glove. I pushed with my left foot. My head came over the edge of the chimney top.

"Thought I – saw you – down there," I gasped.

"Ivan said so," he answered.

I tried to smile with my frozen face. I got my right hand on level ground and pushed. Ang still had my left. My grin faltered, though, as he pulled. It felt like the grip was slipping. I could see from our gloves we were palm to palm, but it felt like I was grabbing the back of his hand. That couldn't be right. Was the glove twisted on his wrist? But his thumb was still at the top of his hand.

It was all wrong.

I looked for the sirdar's eyes behind his sunglasses but all I could see was black. He smiled then and I saw teeth behind teeth.

The glove was slipping off. My right hand scrambled for purchase as my left lost its hold. I tried to swing a leg up onto the ledge but my crampon was hooking on the damn ladder.

"Ang, I'm falling!" I yelled. Panic swelled in my chest, flooded up my neck and found a home behind my eyes. I squeezed the sherpa's hand, fighting the revulsion

35

that accompanied the sensation – was it still a hand I was feeling under that glove? – as my right grip slid across the level ledge toward the abyss.

"What's – what is –? Ivan! Jesus, Ang, help me!"

The hand under the sherpa's glove softened. It felt formless in my desperate grip. And then something as hard as bone, as unforgiving as granite, bulged into my palm. I instinctively let go. Horror was just starting to flood my brain when I realized I'd tipped back too far. For the briefest moment I thought I might recover my balance. But then I fell.

CHAPTER TEN

JUNE 25

THE SEVEN-HOUR CREEP to Askole from Skardu was downright harrowing. Three times Ivan suggested we jump out while the driver maneuvered the truck across a sloping, boulder-choked path that hugged the wall of the river gorge. The Ukrainian said our driver was one of the best. I had no idea what that meant – maybe just that he was completely fatalistic and displayed no fear as his wheels flirted with the void of non-existence.

We reached the village half an hour before the sun dropped behind the mountains. A small tent city waited for us on a strip of grass behind a low stone wall. The head porter stood at the entrance to the paddock and bowed as the truck pulled in.

"His name is Raymond," said Ivan, seated beside me in the Toyota. "That's what we call him, anyway. Good guy. The Baltis listen to him."

Good relations with the porters mattered. I'd read enough mountain literature to know that. You didn't want to get two days into a hike, supplies strewn along a three-mile line of porters, only to have a strike for higher wages. It happened a lot in the early years, when Europeans first came to these mountains. Not that you could blame the porters, not entirely anyway. Sure, it's kind of dodgy saying you'll work for a wage then, when you have the client stuck between a rocky and a steep place, blackmail him for more pay. But you have to think how ridiculous those clients must have appeared – let's face it, how ridiculous I appeared – spending a fortune to stand atop a tall rock. It had to look like madness to a person who just wants a new piece of corrugated steel for his roof or a second cook pot for his fireplace.

My notion of how primitively the porters lived were debunked within minutes of inhabiting the tent city. Generators littered the campground, with plasma screen TVs airing satellite games of soccer from Europe. Some of the Baltis wore sandals and had woollen shawls pulled around their shoulders, sure, but others had North Face soft-shell jackets and Scarpa boots on their feet.

Over supper I asked Ivan how much we were paying the porters.

"Three hundred for the roundtrip."

Ang was with us, as well as his three sherpas and Raymond.

"That sounds low," I said.

"It's not," said Ivan. "It's above market rate. Two hundred to Concordia is standard and Base is only an extra day up and back."

I'm not sure why I cared. Maybe guilt for assuming the locals lived like medieval peasants. Or maybe I just recognized the absurdity of the situation. I was using wealth generated by make-believe currency to employ a party of forty fellow humans to help me die, some of them at risk to their own lives.

"What if we paid them more?" I asked. "Is four hundred dollars good?"

Raymond frowned.

"It's a bad idea," he said. "Porters will wonder how much money you have if you can afford so much. Most will be happy but maybe not all."

"We can discuss it later," said Ivan.

The next morning, as we prepared to head out, the Ukrainian pulled me aside.

"I talked about it with Raymond," he said. "The security situation is not so good. Everyone knows Westerners are rich, but there's regular rich, like climbers who live from one expedition to the next, and then there's fat cat rich. You don't want people to know you're the second. It's a frontier out here, Phil. They have bandits and stuff, marauders on horses and shit. And yes, good old-fashioned greed, too. Maybe a guy who can pay four hundred can also pay a thousand. Don't try to play benefactor to every person we meet."

I don't do charity. I don't give money to homeless people, and when the cashier at the store asks if I want to give two dollars to some cause I always say no. I think I was just scared. My date with fate had me feeling superstitious.

It was bullshit, too. If I actually cared about people, how many of them could I have saved with the six million I was paying Ivan? If some celestial judge was looking down on me, an extra hundred bucks per head wasn't going to be enough, not even close.

It could have been the place itself. The Karakoram felt like another world, like maybe I'd already started my journey away from the land of the living – not to an afterlife, necessarily, but to a place where physics wasn't the same or maybe thoughts had tangible power. It wasn't clear to me what the rules of this new place were, only that the old rules let me down.

I wanted magic even if I didn't believe in it.

Two days walk took us to Paiju, a tiny oasis of green in an immense cathedral of white ice and grey stone. My tent was pitched on sparse grass in the meager shade of a stunted tree. The sherpas dined with Ivan and myself while the Baltis had their own cookfires. It was still light out when I turned in.

Ivan ducked his head into my tent as I zipped into my sleeping bag.

"How are you doing?" he asked.

"Great," I said.

I *did* feel good. Long days outdoors engaged in physical activity, I guess. Cleans out the lungs and arteries. I'd been nursing a headache since that morning but even that wasn't as bad as I'd anticipated.

"I think I'm coping pretty well with the elevation and my feet are fine," I said.

"That's good," he said. "Keep me posted on that. Blisters get bad enough they can hobble you. No intestinal issues?"

He said the last with a smile. We all had intestinal issues. It came with being a foreign traveler in this part of the world.

"Just make sure you stay hydrated and it should pass," he finished.

The next morning took us up onto the glacier. The valley was a mile wide. The mountains on each side stretched into orbit. The toe of the Baltoro was a wall of dirt, ice and stone. A narrow river trickled from under the frozen bed. The top surface was mostly gravel. The ice beneath that layer thickened to hundreds of feet as we gained elevation.

I spent the first day on high alert, still coloured by the caution I'd been taught in Banff. On the glaciers above Bow Lake, you didn't walk ten feet unroped, not unless it was very late in the season and all the snow was gone, revealing the maze of crevasses that criss-crossed the ice fields.

Death in a crevasse would be horrific. If the initial fall didn't kill you, you could be wedged tightly into a glacial vice a hundred or more feet down in the dark. Panic would be hard to resist. You could be trapped upside down. You'd probably break bones as you plunged into the chasm. Hypothermia sets in quickly. If rescue takes too long, or doesn't happen at all, your body could melt the ice and slip deeper into the crevasse. The melted ice refreezes, locking you in a frozen crypt.

The lesson from the Rockies was stark: don't get comfortable on a glacier.

On day two, though, I did start to relax. There were occasional spots where crevasses revealed themselves on the surface, but the dangers were always obvious. The crossings Ang picked were never more than a couple of feet across.

The exotic surface we walked on became commonplace but the surrounding peaks never did. The Trango Tower massif stabbed the sky on the left side of the valley, a sheer face rising more than ten thousand feet from the valley floor.

Grasping the scale of the landscape was impossible. At one point that afternoon Ivan pointed at a low mountain, barely more than a foothill, on the right side of the valley.

"You've been to Bow Lake, right, in Banff? What do they call that mountain, the tall one that looks over the lake?" he asked.

"You mean Crowfoot?" I said.

"Crowfoot. Yes. Well, that little lump you see there is taller than Crowfoot."

I started to smile. "This whole valley is taller," I said. "This glacier is higher than any mountain in Banff."

"I'm not talking about sea level, I'm talking about prominence," he said. "From the foot of that little hill to its crown is higher than the summit of Crowfoot from the surface of Bow Lake."

I couldn't make my eyes understand. The contour in question looked a few hundred feet tall.

"What's it called?" I finally asked.

"Nothing," said the guide. "Around here you don't name mountains that small."

Chapter Eleven

July 16

I DREAMT OF spiders. Spiders as big as horses. Spiders squealing like wild pigs.

I woke in a tent. The air was cold, my breath a cloud of vapour in the orange glow of sunlit tent walls. There was a moment of peace, then confusion – then remembrance and fear.

The hand. The teeth. The fall at the chimney.

"Ivan?" I called out.

I heard a murmur of voices, then, "Phil?"

I sat up, pushed the sleeping bag down around my waist. The tent zipper regurgitated two flaps of fabric as it opened. Ivan stuck his head in.

"What happened to your face?" I asked.

He had a big purple shiner around his right eye.

"You did this," he said. "Turns out you should have been a boxer, not a mountaineer."

Ivan ducked into the shelter and told me the story. How he climbed down to pull me out of the chimney and received a punch in the eye as thanks.

"You've got heavy hands, Phil. I wouldn't have guessed."

That wasn't the end, though. I hung in my harness for fifteen minutes before they tried to help me again. They waited until I was done screaming.

"Ang climbed down to check on you. I was still too pissed off."

"What was I screaming about?"

Ivan raised his eyebrows.

"I didn't say you were yelling words. You were screaming, shrieking like a cheerleader in a slasher movie. It was messed up."

I was stunned. I tried to remember. All I could recall was backwards hands and the sensation of falling into a bottomless, inky abyss.

"I saw something," I managed to say.

"Yeah, you told me that, remember? Just before we reached camp," said the guide.

A wave of disorientation surged up through my stomach to my chest.

"Where are we?" I asked.

41

"Don't remember that either? Camp Two. You insisted on continuing and I didn't want to deal with another freak-out in the chimney. You really don't remember? You seemed okay on the final push."

I shook my head.

"Well, we're here now," said Ivan. "I think we'll stay through today then head back down to ABC tomorrow. I'm gonna climb up to Three, though, back before dark. I want to check how the boys have fixed the Black Pyramid. You're going to rest and keep me posted on how your head is doing."

I nodded at him. "How's *your* head doing?" I asked.

"I'm fine. I think the hard plastic of my goggles caused most of the damage. But let's agree that you won't punch me in the face again, okay?"

I nodded.

"Sorry," I said. "Hey, Ivan – what did I say I saw?"

His head was already out the flap but he stopped and turned back.

"You said Ang wasn't Ang. That's all I could make out."

I wanted to explain but had no explanation. Ivan kept talking.

"It's all good. Is it okay, though, if I send the imposter in with food? Don't leave the tent, not without him. You take one step the wrong way out here and that's it."

"Knock knock," said Ang's voice fifteen minutes later. The sherpa ducked his head into the tent and held out a bowl of hot noodle soup. His broad smile had a single row of teeth, top and bottom, and his eyes, no longer covered by opaque sunglasses, were warm and alert.

The hand holding the bowl, the left hand, there was nothing wrong with it.

"I'll be back. You finish soup, I show you Black Pyramid."

Anyone who's read about K2 and the Abruzzi Ridge knows about the Black Pyramid. It's the toughest section of sustained climbing on the whole route. A thousand feet of genuine rock-climbing. Nothing super challenging, just a few spots with 5.7 moves. What is easy in a gym at sea level, however, is daunting almost four miles off the deck, with snow and ice surfaces, heavy gear and sub-zero temperatures.

Ang made sure I was clipped to an anchor outside the tent before I stepped outside. I stared at his hands as he worked.

He directed my attention to the route above as I stood beside him. I could only make out the first few hundred feet.

"There he is," said the sirdar.

A flash of yellow. Ivan's jacket.

The wall wasn't vertical, at least not the part I could see, but it looked about seventy degrees, possibly more. You'd have little chance of stopping if you fell, not unless you were belayed by a partner or clipped into a fixed rope.

The Black Pyramid has lethal rock fall. Dislodge a small boulder halfway up the wall and death is cascading down on every climber below you. The helmets we wore protected us from gravel, but a ten-pound rock in free-fall would pulverize whatever it hit.

It was the steepness of the route that intimidated me the most. On some mountains, in some spots, you can almost pretend you're climbing up a really big hill. Even a dangerous slope, one that's covered in snow and ready to avalanche, might look safe right up until it killed you.

You can't fool yourself on the pyramid, though. It doesn't even offer the meager shelter of the chimney. There would be spots on the next stretch where I'd be suspended on vertical granite with a thousand empty feet beneath me. Forget to clip in, set an anchor wrong, use a rope that's been stepped on with crampons one too many times, and I'd leave the mountain in pieces.

Yes, pieces. Forget any notion of an intact corpse with a trickle of blood leaking from the mouth. Fall downhill and you accelerate. Sharp boulders and sheer edges are a meat grinder. Legs separate. Arms tear loose. Heads pop off and bounce away.

"Not so bad climb," said Ang. "Just make sure look and look two times."

Ivan was leaning out. Then he disappeared into a shadow.

Ang's assistants had already fixed the whole route, ensuring ropes, pitons and cams offered protection the whole way up the pyramid. Ivan would correct anything he thought was too hard for me. I just needed to handle the mental game. Forget I was on K2 – forget the reputation – and I'd be fine. Unless I wasn't, and then what was I gonna do?

Don't worry until it's too late to worry.

I spent the day in the tent. My knee was a bit sore. I must have banged it when I dropped in the chimney. My head was good, however. If anything, I felt better than usual, almost like the episode had cleared out the pipes or something.

The shelter never warmed up but the golden sunlight still made me drowsy in the early afternoon. I tucked away my reading material – a quarter of a cop novel called The Force, a paperback torn into four equal parts to keep down the weight – and closed my eyes to nap.

I dozed off. When I woke, I caught myself spooning Ivan or Ang. I rolled onto my back, the tent just wide enough to accommodate two. The walls were still bright. I couldn't have been asleep for long. I tried to prop myself up with an elbow. My companion was on his side, facing away from me, cozied up in a mummy-style sleeping bag.

I was thinking about pulling out my scrap of paperback to read more when a sigh came from the sleeping bag. Then a voice I'd never heard before. Mechanical and organic at the same time. Like air passing through a leaking pipe organ.

"We're going to be friends, you and me," said the voice.

I don't think my heart actually stopped but it felt like it. I definitely stopped breathing. Not like when you've taken a lungful of air and held your breath. More like when the wind is knocked out of you: you can't figure out why your damn lungs won't work, all you know is that you're not running the show anymore.

I didn't dare look at the person beside me. I fixed my eyes on the ceiling of the tent.

Who did I think was lying next to me? How do you begin to make sense of the world when the ground splits beneath your feet and a polka-dot dragon emerges? My brain had been launched into the blackest void, pitched into the midnight seas beneath the icy crust of Europa. The sound – the awful, inhuman croak – wasn't even the worst of it. It was the feeling.

Wrong emanated off the figure on a scale I couldn't have imagined.

"You can see me," the sound made words again.

The sleeping bag rolled towards me. I wanted to turn my head away. I screamed in my skull: Look away, please look away! Shut your eyes. You don't want to see this, never!

I stared into the cowl of the sleeping bag and for a moment a single cyclops eye stared back. Then it split like a drop of mercury into a pair of bulging disks. A single hole appeared beneath the two eyes, a pencil-width that expanded into a large oval, big enough to swallow a grapefruit. Translucent teeth – thin needles familiar to entomologists – pushed out of the hole to form a ring around the mouth.

Somehow my body exhaled even further. Stars streaked past as my oxygen-deprived brain fought to stay conscious.

The creature's mouth flattened and started to curve upwards, forming a shape like a kidney bean.

"I can *feel* you," it said.

I screamed. No sound emerged from my mouth, which only seemed to amplify its internal power. A deafening roar consumed my brain, like a million trees being pulverized with an atom bomb.

"Ang, get in here. I think Phil's having a seizure!"

The world had faded to blank grey when my diaphragm finally got the signal to inhale. I took the gulp of air a submariner takes when he emerges surface-side from a sunken vessel.

Ivan was stooped in front of me, his eyes familiar, the concern of a man who protected my life every minute of every day.

"Breathe, my man," said the guide.

I gasped my way through three big inhales. The sleeping bag next to me was empty.

"Where were you?" I finally said.

Ivan misinterpreted, heard judgment.

"What? I was with Ang. I was on the Black Pyramid, Phil. I just got back."

I shook my head and finally got enough breath to speak again.

"Before…thought you were beside me," I gasped.

His turn to shake his head. The tent flap opened and Ang stuffed his face into the shelter.

"Okay okay?" he asked.

I nodded unconvincingly.

"Just a nightmare, I think," I said.

"Yeah, you sure?" said Ivan. "You weren't breathing, bud."

The last thing I needed was for him to think I'd had another episode like the chimney.

"I was holding my breath in the dream," I said. "Guess I made it a little too real."

"You think?" said Ivan.

It took a few more minutes to convince him but finally he shook his head and smiled.

"You are high maintenance, Phil. Anyone ever tell you that?"

I managed a grin.

"My ex-wife. You guys can compare notes when this is done."

Ang announced dinner was ready, over in his tent. I again told both men I was fine and they finally felt secure leaving me.

"Clip into the safety rope before you cross to Ang's tent," said Ivan from outside my door.

I looked at the sleeping bag. Then I unzipped it completely, like a monster might be hiding in the bottom.

45

No one said dying of a brain tumour would be pleasant. If I wanted to avoid crazy – if I wanted reality not to twist, and turn upside down – I should have put a bullet in my head.

Over a supper of rehydrated curry lentils and rice Ivan told us about his day.

"The route is super dry. Good for grip but bad for rockfall. I'm gonna make you take up the rear, Phil. I just can't chance you shaking something loose and dumping it on us."

Funny the things that make you nervous. I'd assumed I'd be climbing the Black Pyramid sandwiched between Ang and Ivan, the two masters a barrier between me and disaster. I supposed it didn't matter. As long as I didn't mess up I'd be safe on the fixed ropes regardless of who was or wasn't underneath me. And if I did forget to clip in, there wasn't much a climber beneath me could do to save the day anyway.

"It's good, though," Ivan continued. "I'll take middle and stay close. There's nothing super hard and your acclimatization is decent."

"I was dying in the chimney," I countered.

"We don't know what happened there," he said, "and everybody struggles the first time they go up it. Mostly the pyramid is just a long day."

Unless you're Ivan. He was up and back down hours before sunset.

"But first we go back down," the guide was still talking. "Advanced Base only – it's too busy in Base Camp now."

He pointed at me.

"It's your fault. The boys were down to Base getting more rope. They had to run a gauntlet of reporters trying to get interviews with the people carrying your sad carcass up the mountain."

I forced a laugh then waited a moment to see if Ivan or Ang would dismiss the notion I was just cargo on this expedition. Neither did.

"It's so insulting," I said as an opening for them.

"Well, they gotta sell their papers, and your story has all the elements: danger, disease and money," said Ivan.

I didn't want to be that guy but I couldn't help myself.

"Do you think they're right? I mean, is this a story about a rich dude buying his way up the mountain?"

Ivan didn't pause or look away.

"Yes and no. You're not Hermann Buhl, okay? Without fixed lines, without logistics, without Ang and I babysitting, this expedition wouldn't have seen Camp One. But for a guy with a brain tumour you've acquitted yourself well. You definitely know more about this mountain than the reporters at basecamp.

"It doesn't really matter anyway. This isn't about them. We've all heard the story of a client on Everest who doesn't know how to attach his own crampons. A person like that may have shown up at Base Camp once or twice, sure. But I guarantee they never made it to the South Col, never mind the summit.

"You climb this beast, Phil, and no one can take that away from you."

CHAPTER TWELVE

JUNE 30

OUR THIRD DAY on the Baltoro we arrived at Concordia, the name given to the patch of glacier where the valleys and rivers of ice meet up. Keep going straight and you'd arrive at the Gasherbrums. Turn left and it's Broad Peak on the right, K2 straight ahead.

The sky was radiant blue but darkness filled the hollows and contours of the lofty slopes above as the setting sun dipped below the towering stone battlements. I was thankful for the clear skies. If the valleys had been filled with clouds – a common occurrence – K2 would have remained concealed. I shuddered at the idea of the great mountain hiding, revealing itself only when I reached Base Camp, its mass emerging from white shrouds of snow or rain – ever taller, the eye climbing higher and higher – too high, the neck craning – only then recognizing a feature still well below the summit, such as the Black Pyramid or the Shoulder.

It was intimidating enough from where we stood, still six hours walk to the foot of the peak.

"What's your first impression?" Ivan asked.

We were standing away from the porters as they set up shelter next to a small cluster of tents belonging to another party.

My thoughts were too bleak to share: I'm almost home. This is where I'll spend eternity. "It's big," I said.

It was mammoth, and also familiar. I picked out features I'd read about. I was especially drawn to the step below the summit where we'd be setting up tents for Camp Four. Referred to as the shoulder, it was a really long way up the mountain. The Black Pyramid rock face below it was even steeper than I expected.

"There's always Broad Peak if you want to change your mind," he joked.

Broad Peak was another 8,000er. It filled most of the right-hand field of vision. It would be a lot less challenging, although the final hundred metres across a knife-edge ridge to its summit sounded every bit as scary as the worst K2 had to offer.

"What are they climbing?" I said.

He looked back at the cluster of tents already set up when we arrived.

"This is as far as they go. Trekkers from Wales. Used to be a dozen tents here most of the season. Sometimes more. People are nervous. First thing they asked was if we'd had trouble on the way."

I snorted, like the idea was ridiculous.

"Honestly, I wondered if we might," he continued. "This is disputed territory. There hasn't been any action right here this season, but last year some climbers were collateral damage in a skirmish near Muztagh Tower. Four people dead."

He said it matter-of-factly, as if he was talking about a mild misfortune.

"Do you worry about it – the risk?" I said.

He shrugged.

"You have a lot of money and I've lost a lot of friends in the mountains. I'd rather die on the slopes than be blown up, sure, but we're all leaving one way or another. If danger was going to keep me away from the Karakoram, I never would have come here in the first place. Besides..."

He fanned his right arm in the direction of K2.

"...how could I not come back? She's a terrible beauty."

I had a staggering headache the next morning. I had trouble keeping my breakfast down. I was jittery, too, about our final approach. We were really here. I'd made my plan and now I had to live and die with it.

We were on the move before sunlight reached the floor of the valley, a long line of headlamps illuminating what looked like an endless gravel pit. Each step jolted my brain. I didn't say much about it to Ivan. I didn't need to. He gave me two extra-strength ibuprofen. I kept my hand extended. He gave me one more.

"It's not like I'm going to need my liver much longer anyway," I quipped.

Our destination filled the sky ahead. It didn't seem to be getting taller as we walked but it widened until everything you saw was K2. In a strange way the mountain looked squatter the closer we got. Ivan said it was just a trick of perspective.

"Foreshortening," he said during a rest. "When we get close, the higher parts of the mountain seem to get smaller. The upper slopes aren't as near as they look. That spot there—" he pointed out the top of a buttress "—looks like it's, what, three-quarters of the way up the mountain? It's not. That's Camp One on the Cesen route."

Ivan looked at me looking at the mountain as I tried to process his words.

"Now you're starting to understand," he said.

The way he said the words I knew he wasn't just talking about foreshortening.

I was doing something a person with my level of experience never does. I wasn't Henry Ford placed behind the steering wheel of a Corvette. I was more like Orville Wright suddenly dropped into the lunar lander as it touches down in the Sea of Tranquility. As we sat there staring at the mountain an avalanche broke loose to the left of the Cesen route. Millions of pounds of ice, snow and rock cascaded down a vertical couloir. The sound was a muted rumble.

Ivan clapped me on the shoulder.

"You're going to love it," he said. "You'll be scared shitless but you'll love it."

I saw the tents of K2 Base Camp an hour later. I was expecting a tight cluster but they were spread out. The lower slopes kept growing with each step. I couldn't believe how steep it was. I knew it would be more than forty-five-degrees, but I had no frame of reference for what that really meant. The route we would be taking, the Abruzzi, looked almost vertical from our vantage point.

The Duke of Abruzzi was one of the first Europeans to try scrambling up the slopes of K2. Aleister Crowley, the notorious occultist, attempted the peak in 1902, seven years before the Italian foray. As for locals, who knows how high anyone ever made it? Mountain people traditionally had a practical attitude towards their surroundings: stay in the valleys unless you have a good reason to go uphill. Hidden away in some of the most inaccessible and perilous terrain on the planet, K2 likely went untouched until the modern era.

The Abruzzi Ridge is the most popular route, but it's far from safe. The ratio of summits to deaths following the duke's footsteps is four to one. The duke never got that far up the ridge named in his honour. It was another group of Italians who finally achieved the first summit in 1953.

Our path would follow mixed rock, snow and ice up to Camp Two. After that came the Black Pyramid. Camp Three was just below the shoulder. Base Camp would look like a series of coloured pinpoints from that lofty height. Any sense of relief gained from being off the pyramid would be offset by the menace of the steep snow slope above. It was prime avalanche territory.

The final camp, Four, was on the Shoulder, ideally a good ways up that feature to shorten summit day. Then through the Bottleneck, across the traverse and a final, gasping push up the snowfields to the top. For people who needed to make it back alive, the whole thing then had to be done in reverse, in an even more pronounced state of exhaustion, hypoxia, dehydration and starvation. It wasn't unusual for climbers to lose twenty or thirty pounds over a six-week expedition.

It was cold at the foot of K2. A brisk wind whipped down the slopes. A pennant of mist hurricaned off the summit more than twelve thousand feet above us.

A dozen tents were spread across the valley just ahead. Ivan was a hundred metres in front of me. He had this way of walking where his legs moved languidly yet he covered ground at a brisk rate. He pulled ahead in the final kilometre then stopped and waited for me to join him.

"This is our spot," he said when I reached him.

It looked like moraine but wasn't. Moraine was heaped rock and gravel left behind by a glacier when it retreats but we were still on top of the glacier and would be until we started climbing. It had the same appearance, though, with sand dune-shaped piles of scree and pea-gravel gullies.

It was a place not meant for life, like a desolate, alien planet in one of the old Star Trek episodes. But a feeling of joy welled up in my chest. I wanted to smile and cry and laugh. I bottled it up instead. It was enough just to feel the warmth tingling in my arms and belly.

"I'm so glad I'm here," was all I said.

CHAPTER THIRTEEN

JULY 17

RAYMOND MET US when we got back down to ABC from Camp Two. All of Ang's sherpa assistants were there, as well, the first time since our arrival at the mountain.

"You do good job," said Tsering, grabbing me in a rough hug as we walked into camp. Thirty years old, he was the eldest of Ang's young team. His brother, Dawa, was the junior-most member of our party at nineteen. You could tell they were family, with faces narrower than typical among their people, and the same bright eyes.

"It was tough. The chimney was hard going up and hard coming down," I replied.

Tsering gripped my shoulders.

"You still here. Good climb. Good climber," he said.

The compliment meant a lot. I thanked him but Raymond approached with a tray of cups before I could say more. Steam rose from the lacquered metal mugs into the wintry summer air.

"It's good to see you, Ray, thank you," I said to our camp manager as I reached for a mug.

"And you, sir," he said, always formal.

Ivan disappeared into the largest tent, a tall affair that housed the kitchen and food that had been ferried from Base, as well as extra gear, including a computer with sat-linkup for weather reports and email.

Ang handed his pack off to one of the sherpas – the shortest one, Nawang – then took a cup from Ray's platter. Raymond said something. I didn't catch it but a look of concern crossed Ang's face. The sherpa nodded and looked down – like the ground might contain an answer – then walked around the main tent towards his sleeping shelter.

I asked Raymond what was going on.

"Everything," he said. "Every day another chopper brings a TV crew hoping for an interview with you."

He read the surprise in my expression.

"It's good you are staying here at ABC," he said. "It's crazy. I haven't seen Base Camp so busy since before the war – except instead of climbers, it's reporters. No journalists arrived yesterday, though. Maybe it's slowing down."

"But what about Ang?"

"The only person who came yesterday was another Nepalese with a message for Ang. His infant son is unwell."

I was immediately concerned. I cared about Ang, of course. I cared about his baby, too, in the vague way that every adult is supposed to care about really young humans they don't know. I was past lying to myself, though. We were getting to a critical point in the expedition. Our next trip up would take us to Camp Three for an overnight, and the trip after that should be the summit push, weather permitting. My strength – what little I had – felt contingent on the presence of my two leaders, Ivan and Ang. Having them on my team was like stepping onto a basketball court with LeBron James and Michael Jordan flanking me. They could carry my sorry carcass all the way to the championship.

I tried not to get ahead of myself. Ang's boy was sick. That's what I knew. Nervous speculation about what that might mean for our adventure was wasted energy.

I retreated to my own tent to change into camp clothes. It was still frigidly cold, so I was really exchanging one set of winter gear for another, but it still felt good to strip off my rancid base layer and put on fresh long johns and a clean thermal shirt.

A change of clothes was a luxury. I changed my sock liners and underwear every day when we climbed but that was it. Same base layer, same insulating layer and same shell jacket and pants day after day. The extras we carried in our packs were to respond to changing conditions – thinner gloves or thicker, for example – not to indulge the luxury of clean clothing. My skin responded to this regimen of filth by developing patches of scaly fungal infections on my chest, the back of my legs and my groin. Nothing really miserable – no open sores – but damn itchy.

Ivan was back in the lounge – that's what he called the largest tent – when I entered.

"This weather is unbelievable," he said. He was seated at the table looking at the computer. "Best season on record. Look at these stats. Less snow, more sunshine. There's been warmer years, sure, but none with clearer skies."

Ivan said it wasn't unusual to be stranded at Base for a week or more waiting for a weather window.

"Back in 2009, not a single person summited all season, and it wasn't for lack of trying."

I interrupted to ask about Ang's child.

"Yeah, he's already headed down to Base to get more information," said Ivan. He didn't turn from his laptop. "But he'll be right back. Ang might be the only person I know who's more determined and less sentimental than I am. I don't think it will affect us."

He looked up at me.

"It's okay to be selfish," he said.

"Does that make me a bad person?" I asked.

He gave a small smile.

"Consider it a further step along your path to the full madness of mountaineering. Everything else in life becomes smaller, Phil, and all that's left is the need to send. I can't explain it. I definitely can't justify it. These stupid hills become everything and that's it."

Ivan and I got drunk after supper. The sherpas got hammered.

The youngsters were used to fermented millet, a nasty-tasting drink that contains some alcohol but not enough to justify the unpleasant flavour. At ABC, though, we kept the selection simple. Raymond didn't drink – he was Muslim – but apparently he knew great whisky: the battered cooler contained eight bottles, including my personal favourite, Tortmore '98.

As Ray prepared our first tumblers of the night, he shared that the ice he was using came from the glacier.

"It began its life on top of the mountain," he said.

"To a taste of the summit!" Ivan bellowed.

I didn't know if the sherpas cared about glacier ice but they were happy to share the booze. I'm sure some Nepalese can drink like frat boys but not our lads. They were red-faced and roaring by the time we were cracking the second bottle, a high-end Suntory that would offend Scotch purists but tasted to this slob like it was casked in the Outer Hebrides.

In some ways beer would have been a bigger luxury. The same porter could carry forty-eight cans of beer from Askole or twenty bottles of hard liquor. Later that night I asked Raymond to bring in a case of Fuller's beer for our end-of-expedition celebration. In my drunken state, the notion of a porter bearing porter struck me as funny.

The second bottle was half empty. The younger men were dancing, gathered around a portable stereo sagging in a fabric camp stool. Ivan and I were parked in two foldout chairs.

"I saw something at Camp Two," I said.

I'd been thinking about it. Of course I'd been thinking about it. I thought being drunk would banish the memory, but I could still hear the voice. I could still feel the fear.

"Yeah? What's that?" said Ivan.

I liked Ivan in camp. On the mountain, he was my parent. We were not colleagues. He was a benevolent tyrant. I did as he commanded and tried to meet his expectations. But in camp we were, if not equal, a lot closer to it.

"I saw someone in the tent."

"Yeah, I thought that nightmare story was horseshit," said the guide.

I gave an apologetic smile.

"I figured I'd given you enough to worry about already," I said.

Ivan rubbed his black eye. It had darkened and spread.

"Well, no point in keeping secrets," he said. "And don't worry about seeing things. Everyone sees things in the mountains. Why should a guy with a brain tumour be any different?"

I told him what happened. I told him about the voice.

"It wasn't human," I said. "It wasn't something I would imagine, either. Hell, I don't even have words to describe it."

Ivan shrugged.

"All right," he said.

"All right?"

He took a big mouthful of scotch, emptying his glass.

"Sure. I mean, look at it from my perspective. Either the guy with cancer in his head is hallucinating a little when he's oxygen-deprived. *Or* Stephen King writes non-fiction. You see where I'm coming from?"

I nodded. Of course it wasn't real. I wasn't entirely comforted, though. Being so far gone that my imagination conjured monsters from thin air was pretty scary.

"You're not crazy," said the guide. "I mean, you probably are – you're climbing K2 – but seeing the boogeyman doesn't make you nuts. Climbers imagine people all the time. It's a phenomenon known as the third man."

He told me then about a climb he did in Alaska. It was an unnamed peak and he left it that way, even though he was the first one to the summit.

"I was done. I'd rapped down two thousand feet using my last ice screw to bore out v-threads the whole way down. No food for three days. Fuel gone, water gone. Oh, and I was on the wrong side of the mountain."

His route dropped him in a jumbled icefall.

"It was bad, man. No business being there. I don't get scared climbing, and I was scared. Too tired, too strung out, composure just gone. In twenty-five years of expeditions that's the only time I truly believed I wasn't going to make it."

It was hard for me to imagine that thought ever crossing Ivan's mind.

"So I see this fella headed the same way as me – he's out for a walk, just like me – and I tell him I'm thinking about taking a long break, just shutting the whole thing down and going to sleep in a crevasse. He tells me to walk with him instead, so I do."

His new friend stuck by his side all the way to treeline.

"It's vivid, Phil. I can see his face. I know his voice. And he never existed. There was no one else on that mountain. The nearest human was a hundred miles away. But he was real for a few hours. And then I was safe. I was alive and he was gone."

"You're not saying this was some kind of angel or something?" I asked.

He grinned.

"There're no angels," he said. "Devils, sure – I've met a few – but there are no angels. It was just me looking after me. It's you looking after you."

I nodded. I didn't tell him what I was thinking: how was frightening myself with horrible visions a survival strategy?

We'd opened a third bottle – I didn't need another drink but you couldn't tell me that – when Ang came through the tent flap.

"Woohoo! The man is back!" I yelled.

Raymond's frown and Ivan's squeeze on my arm were a dose of instant sobriety.

"Shit, I'm sorry," I muttered lamely.

Ang's face registered no response. He didn't even look at me. He didn't look at Ivan either.

"I need to eat," he said to the room, then crossed the tiny floor to the tabletop where food was stacked.

"Sorry, man," said Ivan. His voice sharpened when he asked Dawa to turn down the boom box.

Ang frowned.

"It is okay," said the sirdar. "Nima will be okay."

He didn't look like his son was okay. It suddenly occurred to me that maybe I was supposed to be making some sort of gesture. Should I release him from his contract? Should I offer to fly him home for a visit? Or do both, and pay him the full amount for the job, too?

He didn't work for me, though, he worked for Ivan. I guess it was a technicality. Ivan could pay him even though the job wasn't complete and I could reimburse Ivan. But Ivan was wealthier than me by far – or at least he would be when the expedition finished and I gave him most of my money – and he wasn't saying anything.

The party didn't resume. Ang sat on a folding chair and stared into space as he ate a bowl of leftover curry rice. One of the sherpas turned off the music and they all filtered silently out of the tent. I didn't know what to do.

"Go to bed," Ivan told me. "Weather looks good tomorrow so we're up at five. I want to reach Camp Two in a single push. You need a long, tough day, get you mentally ready for the big event."

A shot of adrenaline pumped into my spine at the mention of our final goal.

I was scared. I wouldn't let it paralyze me, though. I'd use fear to keep me sharp, keep me motivated.

CHAPTER FOURTEEN

JULY 1

WE TOOK AN inventory upon our arrival at Base Camp.

It's amazing how much stuff it takes to support even a small expedition. Tons of food and lots of fuel. Tents and more tents, sleeping bags and sleeping pads. Ivan arranged for us to use the fixed ropes of another expedition at the top of the mountain, where the Cesen and Abruzzi routes met. We still needed to fix lots of rope on the lower slopes, though, which meant stakes and ice screws, pitons and hammers, as well as a large selection of trad gear, such as nuts and cams.

I'd carried most of my personal kit up the Baltoro Glacier. If it was too heavy to haul on level ground, it was too heavy to take up the Abruzzi. Mountaineering is a dream for gear heads. My standard setup for a day on the slopes included an ice axe, harness, mountaineering boots and crampons, four carabiners, a sling, two cords that could be tied into prussic knots to ascend ropes, and a rappel device to descend quickly. I also carried an ice screw and a jumar – used to ascend ropes – a walking pole, a helmet and a pocket knife. A slim backpack held two litres of water, a bit of food and some toilet paper, a sleeping pad, and a contribution to the group effort, such as a fuel canister.

Clothing for the day varied. On warm days, I got away with climbing pants and gaiters, a wool undershirt and a soft-shell jacket. Most days required heavier layers. My outfit for the summit looked like something an astronaut might wear, with multiple layers buried beneath a full down suit.

Much of what we unpacked at Base Camp needed to go uphill. The sherpas would haul the bulk of it, which offends purists and laypeople alike. I was happy to give the hardcore alpinists their due – they had knowledge and ability I'd never have – but I couldn't care less about the couch critics. You heard it all the time about Everest. Spectators think having someone carry your tent to the South Col is tantamount to a gondola ride to the summit. They couldn't be more wrong. No one walks up one of the planet's fourteen giants without working harder than they ever thought possible.

We didn't have oxygen. Some K2 climbers use it, including the first pair to summit back in 1953, but most don't. I didn't look down on using 'O's but I didn't want to. Having my tent carried to Camp Four didn't offend my sense of fair play but using oxygen for some reason did.

The porters, under the guidance of Raymond, had our camp in order two hours after we arrived. Raymond was staying on as cook for the expedition while the other Baltis were headed back to Askole the next morning. They would return to collect whatever kit and survivors remained.

The core team gathered in the mess tent for supper that first night. Ivan was a little drunk. I'd seen him fish a bottle of bourbon out of a crate within twenty minutes of the porters' arrival.

"I would like to propose a toast," he announced to the table after Raymond placed the fourth heaped serving dish on it.

The guide wasn't drinking alone. He'd poured two fingers for each of us: Ang and the four sherpas, as well as myself. Only Raymond abstained.

"To the leader of our expedition, Phil...," Ivan began.

"You're the leader, I'm not the leader," I objected.

"...the leader of our expedition: may he have the strength and courage to find what he is looking for. You're a crazy bastard, Phil, but we're all here to help and we're all rooting for you. To the top!"

"To the top!" we cheered and bounced plastic cups together.

Ivan let us sleep-in the next morning. After a late breakfast, the sherpas invited us to participate in a puja ceremony. A small cairn of rocks had been erected from which prayer flags were strung. I can't say I felt especially enlightened after throwing rice three times and spreading sampa on Ivan's face, but it was obviously important to my eastern teammates to seek permission for the climb from their mountain gods.

After the puja, Ivan invited me to join him for a walk to another rock cairn.

I followed Ivan's footsteps as we crossed the Godwin-Austen Glacier. Ang came along. I heard the Gilkey Memorial before I saw it, a muted clank of metal brushed by the wind. I knew what made that sound. It's a tradition for the teammates of fallen climbers to use a hammer and nail to punch letters on a tin plate and hang it on the memorial.

Actually reaching the cairn involved a scramble up a couple hundred feet to a ledge. Ivan placed his hands on the original stone edifice. Memorial plates, plaques and other small monuments had spread to fill the area around the pile of rocks erected by Art Gilkey's teammates in 1953.

Gilkey died on an American expedition after developing a blood clot in his leg high on the mountain. His team tried to get him down, forgoing the chance to be first on K2's summit. Gilkey didn't make it and his team narrowly escaped death.

"This is the second time I have seen this place," said Ivan. "What about you, Ang?"

"Four time. Smell is bad."

There was an odor. I couldn't quite place it. I'd noticed it the day before as we'd walked into base.

"What *is* that?" I asked Ivan.

"I'll show you on the way back," he said.

I read the names on the plates and plaques, some of them familiar from books I owned. It wasn't until we were climbing back down that it occurred to me: My name would soon join them. An entire lifetime reduced to a tin plate and a hundred and seventy pounds of frozen meat somewhere high on the mountain.

I might have been wrong about that very last part, though. We'd walked five minutes across the glacier in the direction of camp when Ivan pointed out something I'd missed on the way up to the memorial. A scrap of navy blue fabric emerged from the dirt covering the ice. He waved for me to join him.

"The smell. It's this. Pieces of climbers. Look, it's a hand. A hand and the cuff of a jacket."

God, he was right. I didn't even put it together until he told me. Yes, those brown sticks emerging from the cloth – they were mummified fingers.

"They're all over here," Ivan continued. "No one stays on the slopes. Ice and snow sheds off the mountain and ends up here."

The bodies get frozen in ice, he explained. The ice cracks apart and so do the corpses. Pieces of climbers.

"More than eighty people have died on K2 and probably half of them are under our feet," he said. "A bit here, a bit there. They move fast, too. We're a ways from the foot of the mountain."

I might not be a frozen sentinel greeting mountaineers for centuries to come. I could be processed, reduced, like so many casualties before me. What had been a faint odor suddenly seemed much stronger. It clung to the back of my mouth, stuck in my throat. I shuffled away from Ivan's grim lesson, my feet stumbling to find level on the uneven terrain.

I am nothing, however, if not a master of self-deception. I pushed that afternoon's revelation into a deep closet in my brain. By next morning, when Raymond woke me with a cup of coffee just before dawn, I found myself in great spirits for our first foray to the start of the Abruzzi route.

Ten minutes' walk took us past the tents of the other teams. The Italians were there in force. There was a smaller Spanish team, and a group of Asians I later found out were from Taiwan. Only a couple of people were outside, though, and we didn't stop for conversation, other than to nod and say hello in low voices. As soon as we passed the last tent, Ivan told me to halt.

"We're going to rope up here. We take nothing for granted beyond this point. People have died close to home."

I knew of one case at least. The name escaped me. He was Italian, I think. Tried to solo a new route. Didn't get to the summit but survived the hazards of high altitude only to fall to his death within sight of Base Camp.

Ang was behind me. That was our usual lineup on the rope. Me sandwiched in the middle.

Our route took us along the base of the mountain. Climbers with dreams of summiting Everest face one of their biggest challenges right outside Base Camp: the Khumbu Icefall, a cascading, groaning smashup of giant seracs. K2's icefall is less notorious but still requires intense focus.

"You'll go over this route again and again. Complacency is one of the biggest dangers in this environment," said Ivan.

It was hard to imagine becoming complacent.

Sunlight still hadn't reached the valley floor two hours later. Ivan stopped. Three tents were set up far enough away from the slope to avoid rockfall, although avalanches were still a threat.

"This is Advanced Base. We'll return here tonight," said Ivan. "Leave your sleeping bag. You'll need water and food, and a fuel canister for Camp One."

The guide indicated the tent I would be using. I dumped my excess load. Ivan waved me over when I emerged. He pointed straight up the slope. I couldn't make out the peak from this close up, just slopes of ice and jagged rock extending to the sky. Snow-covered scree and black boulders waited for us. Large outcrops of sheer rock striated the steep mountainside.

"We're climbing to Camp One today. We'll boil some water when we get there and hang out for a couple hours, then come back down. Climb high, sleep low. You know the drill."

Over a span of weeks we would climb higher and higher, each time sleeping as low as practicably possible. Before our summit attempt, we'd return to the bottom for a rest, a last chance to fuel our bodies with life-giving oxygen before the dash up the mountain.

"Why are we camped so close? Couldn't an avalanche hit us?" I asked.

He nodded. "It's a calculated risk. If you want to be close to the start of the route, you need to be close to the mountain. But you're right, avalanches can come right through here, and I should know."

Ivan pointed just past our tents.

"That's where I ended up. On our descent from climbing the summit serac, Ang and I were almost to the bottom – we were coming out of that couloir right up there – when the slope let go. Nothing we could do. Nothing. We weren't even roped together. We dropped almost a thousand feet…"

"It doesn't look that high up," I said, peering uphill to the point he'd indicated.

Ivan smiled. "Tell me that in an hour when we've reached it."

The guide continued his story. Both of them were swept down the mountain to a point just past where we'd established our Advanced Base Camp.

"…and when we stopped moving, only my right leg was buried. Ang was almost covered but his left arm was sticking straight out of the snow, plain to see."

The sirdar was putting something in a bag outside his tent and walked over to see what we were discussing.

"I had him dug out in less than a minute," Ivan finished, "neither of us with a scratch. Avalanche or not, this spot is good luck."

Ang frowned.

"No good luck," he said. "Bad place."

The sherpa walked away.

I raised my eyebrows at Ivan.

"That doesn't sound good," I said.

Ivan shrugged. "He's superstitious and the mountain has lots of stories. Some of them are true. Lots of them are bullshit. I believe Yves LaPlanche dropped dead from a heart attack at this spot after a nasty three-day descent from the summit. I believe it because people have heart attacks and I've read the book detailing that expedition. The story about Aleister Crowley, though, contains about as much truth as any other story about a magician conjuring demons." That caught my attention. I knew next to nothing about the occult figure. I remembered reading Jimmy Page of Led Zeppelin owned a home in Scotland once owned by Crowley. I was surprised when I'd learned he was a mountaineer. Not exactly the pastime I would have expected for a bohemian sensualist. He was on K2 in 1902 and Kanchenjunga in 1905. The latter expedition went sour – some kind of falling out between teammates – and there was a fatal accident, although I couldn't remember the details.

"Crowley stayed right here?" I asked.

Ivan frowned.

"No. Maybe? Hell, I dunno. I'm pretty sure, though, he didn't carve up a porter on that boulder and feed him to vultures to enlist the help of Satan."

I pointed at the picnic table-sized rock he'd indicated. It was just outside of camp, between us and the slope.

"Jesus, you don't really mean that actual...?"

"Oh yes I do. Ang won't touch it. None of the sherpas will."

I walked over to the large stone. It was a rounded triangle, a foot off the ground at the close edge, rising to a couple of feet on the far side. Three deep gouges marred the broad, flat surface.

"It has these marks," I said.

"Yes, it does. Apparently Crowley had the strength of Thor when he dropped a cleaver on his victim."

I looked at the rock. I looked for red stains, like the story was not only true, but evidence of the unholy crime might have survived more than a century.

"Not Satan," Ang called from the entrance to his tent. "Rakshasa."

"What?" I said.

"A bad spirit," said Ivan. "These are stories, Phil, just stories. Some locals see yetis on these slopes. Others imagine witchcraft and murder. This mountain will cast you far into the depths of fear and extremity, and it doesn't care if you make it back to shore."

The slope began just beyond camp. It was immediately steep. Ang's helpers had fixed ropes almost down to the tent site. We didn't hook onto them. Ivan said we could move uphill quicker as a rope team, we'd use the fixed ropes to descend.

Ivan promised we would go slow – and I knew it was very slow by his standards – but the pace was murderous for me. Within ten minutes of starting the ascent my heart rate was one-fifty and it stayed there for the next four hours of climbing. The headache was constant, of course, barely worth mentioning. Was it caused by altitude or cancer? Probably both. What amazed me, though, was how short of breath I felt. I'd read that breathing in the death zone above 8,000 metres was like trying to suck air through a drinking straw, but I felt like that at 17,000 feet, almost ten thousand feet lower.

Rests were infrequent. Five minutes each hour. Ivan told me speed was safety. Every second you were on the hill you were exposed to danger. The biggest threat was falling debris. That was a reason to climb early in the day. The overnight freeze kept things in place. By late afternoon, ice melts and objects start dropping.

"Situational awareness is key, Phil. You have to know what is happening in front of you, what your teammate is doing below, and what's threatening you from above."

Ivan was talking on our second break. Already the glacier was far beneath us.

"These helmets might stop little stuff, but for big stuff they're useless. Any rock larger than your fist is a potential killer, so stay on your toes."

I should have been scared. A part of me was, I suppose. But the adrenaline coursing through me felt more like excitement than fear. I was climbing to Camp One on K2!

This was the place. Not the place where I would die – that wasn't the focus of my thoughts that day – but the mountain I'd revered ever since I saw that photo of it taken during the 1909 expedition.

This was the mountain the world's greatest mountaineers dreamt about.

Wind blew spindrift across our faces. Small stones clattered past. No life could be seen anywhere accept our three bright figures. It was a trap, a tomb, a siren luring us on, yet it also felt like home. Somehow I belonged in this place. I was doing what I was supposed to be doing and that feeling pasted a smile on my face the whole miserable climb up to Camp One.

Three small tents perched precariously on a sloping ledge of snow, shielded overhead by a shelf of rock. Ivan stayed roped to me the whole time, even when we doffed our crampons and crept into one of the tents. My mouth was parched and my muscles starved.

Melting snow for water, soup and coffee is one of the most time-consuming tasks on an expedition. Dehydration will kill. It's also, to some extent, inevitable, especially on a summit push. You can't hydrate from eating snow. You'd need to eat a ton of it and melting that much snow in your body would dangerously lower your core temperature. Stove fuel is vital. Run out of fuel and your time on the mountain is done.

As Ivan prepared soup, I asked him why the other teams weren't on our route, the Abruzzi. The Cesen intersected our path at the shoulder, sharing Camp Four before tackling the summit pyramid.

"The Cesen is my preferred route, actually," he said. "I think it's safer. But we couldn't get a permit – already full with the other expeditions. We're the only ones on the Abruzzi this season."

The return to Advanced Base Camp was accomplished quickly using our rappelling devices. After a day of rest, we ascended again to Camp One to stay overnight. Then back down to ABC, where a forecasted snowstorm moved in and dumped two feet of fresh fall on us. With snow expected for the rest of the week, Ivan moved us back to Base Camp.

I was starting to feel like a mountaineer. I found myself comparing my experience to the experience of imaginary climbers back in Canada: how much did I know about mountaineering now compared to the people I'd shared the Bow Hut with back in my intro week? I wasn't a real mountaineer – not yet – but would climbing House's Chimney earn me that title? What about the Black Pyramid? Surely tackling K2's Bottleneck would be sufficient to award myself an imaginary trophy?

It was ridiculous, of course. Yet it did serve a positive purpose: I forgot about cancer.

I spent entire days barely thinking about it. Even snowbound at Base Camp, I enjoyed the easy camaraderie of my teammates. We shared a meal with the Taiwanese team, got drunk with the Spanish one night. It was summer camp with the cool kids. I even developed a crush on one of the Spanish girls, which just meant I spoke to her less than the others and made a conscious effort to appear disinterested.

Life felt present, and each day seemed important. We had simple, dangerous tasks to accomplish and when our work was done, we ate heartily and felt satisfied. If we snoozed all afternoon in our tents, we weren't being lazy, we were recuperating.

It felt like I could live that way forever.

PART II

CHAPTER FIFTEEN

JULY 18

ANG CAME WITH coffee before sunrise. My head throbbed. Too much scotch at our little team shindig the night before.

I thanked him and he nodded. His face was blank, his eyes wet stones. Something felt different. His gaze made me feel like a specimen, like he was observing me from an impossible distance. A Martian perched atop Olympus Mons.

At breakfast, when Ang ducked out to pee, I told Ivan the sherpa wasn't right. It was just us in the tent, Raymond and the climbing crew gone before I woke up – Ray back to Base and the other sherpas headed uphill.

"He's fine," said Ivan.

"He's not fine," I said. "He's freaking out. His boy has to be really sick. I think we need to let him go."

"We're not doing that," said Ivan. "He wouldn't quit if I told him to. The mountains are where climbers like us come when everything else goes to shit. This is exactly where he should be. It's no favour sending him away."

I started to say more but Ivan held up a hand to stop me.

"This is a waste of time, Phil. We've got a long way to climb and I'm making the call." A quarter of an hour later Ivan was outside my tent asking if I was ready to go. Nervousness squeezed my innards. I told him I'd meet him in ten minutes. I spent nine of those ten minutes voiding my bladder and bowels, then met my two climbing partners on the other side of camp.

I felt tired and stiff. It took an hour of climbing to warm up. I'd finally found a comfortable rhythm by the time we reached Camp One. I was warm enough to remove my outer shell and climb with just a fleece over my base layer. Ang was leading the way and Ivan was behind me, a rope team of three with fifteen metres between each of us. The fixed ropes between ABC and One were still in place but we didn't hook on. Ivan didn't think we needed the added security.

We paused for ten minutes at the Camp One tents. My companions grabbed extra fuel and a sleeping bag that needed to go higher. We rested long enough to down half a litre of water and a couple of chalky-tasting, half-frozen nutrition bars. Rest too long and the cold settles in. I'd built up a sweat on the trek up and the moisture on my skin drew heat from my body as we stood still. I'd warm up once we got moving, so I didn't bother putting my shell back on. Ivan made a verbal check with each of us, took the lead from Ang, and we were off again.

The route above One was as steep as the route below, but the footing was worse. We were encountering a lot of blue ice. Ivan decided to hook us onto the fixed rope. An ice axe is pretty useless for self-arrest on ice. The pick needs to plunge in to act as a brake, but dropping your bodyweight onto your axe – standard practice for self-arresting – accomplishes little on ice. The most you'll likely achieve is leaving a nice long scratch in the surface as you slide to your death.

Crampons, however, are vital. Ivan was planting his front points into the sixty-degree slope as he kicked his way higher. One of his hands gripped the handle of his ascender and the other drove the sharpened point on the haft of his axe down into the slope to create an extra balance point.

I had to request a stop after ten minutes. I put on my outer layer. I was really cold and the wind was picking up. It was awkward getting the shell out of my bag while balancing on the steep slope. My calves were burning. I should have followed Ang's example. As soon as we stopped, he used the adze side of his axe to chop a narrow step where he could stand flat-footed.

I finally got my jacket on but the shivering that had begun right after our break at One didn't let up. I needed to get moving, get blood circulating.

The rope rounded a rock outcropping. When I came around the corner, Ang was waiting.

"Avalanche here. No fix rope," he said.

There should have been another line beginning where the one we were on ended. Fixers place ropes so you never have to be unattached, you just move one carabiner from the current rope to the new one, then the second carabiner once the first is secure. No break in the chain of protection.

The next rope was gone. Above us an open slope was snow-covered, with striations and little nuggets of snow-ice marking its surface.

"Wait for Ivan," said Ang.

The guide was only fifty feet back. It probably wasn't more than a minute before he joined us. But that minute of inactivity was enough to turn the sweat on my chest to ice.

"No rope," Ang called to the man when he came into view.

Ivan didn't bother answering until he'd crossed the final five metres. With the wind gusting to 80 kilometres an hour, it was hard to hear someone until they were right beside you.

"Rope's buried?" said Ivan.

Ang nodded.

The rope was still there but under three feet of snow. The moment the avalanche stopped moving, the slurry of ice and snow set like cement. It would need to be dug out. Ivan didn't want to take the time.

"We'll rope up," he said. "Chimney's only a few pitches away. We're not spending all day messing around with this."

I looked uphill but couldn't make out the cliff that housed House's Chimney. Spindrift blew everywhere, leaching its way into hoods, and between gloves and sleeves. Visibility was down to thirty yards or so.

Ivan made a figure-eight on a bight and handed it to me to clip in.

"You're shivering," he said. "Feel okay?"

I told him I was fine. I was freezing, of course, but that wasn't the kind of thing I felt like admitting to Ivan or Ang. Complaining about the cold is something children do. Being a mountaineer means being prepared for anything; you make smart gear choices and have enough fortitude and courage to storm the gates of Hell, as long as the Devil has a mountain in there that needs to be climbed.

This time Ivan led the way. He didn't bother with switchbacks, just tackled the steep slope head on. My calves were burning and so were my lungs as we trudged up the snow-covered slope.

The avalanche must have been a monster. We were well past the length of one rope and most of the length of another before Ivan stepped back onto ice. This time, though, the rope wasn't buried. It was just gone.

Not the kind of thing that happens often. Usually ropes are anchored with nuts (for rocks) or screws (in ice). In snow, however, a picket is usually the best option. The only problem with a snow picket is that it moves if the snow moves.

The slope was clean of snow. This was where the slab broke loose that buried the rope lower down. More blue ice underfoot as we swung our crampons into the slope.

I could finally make out the low cliff above. The chimney was close. Damn that cold, though. I was frozen right through. As soon as we reached the bottom of the chimney, I'd tell Ivan I needed to warm up. We were making good time. We could take shelter in the rocks, get out of the wind and cook some noodles or something, and then tackle the hundred-foot vertical ascent.

Have you ever been walking down the street behind someone when they trip? They recover their balance, then turn around and stare at the ground where they lost their footing. Invariably there's nothing there – no fist-sized rock, banana peel or piano wire strung across the path – it was their own clumsiness.

The ice was not to blame, but I didn't have time to scowl at it anyway. I placed my foot eight inches up the mountainside, shifted my weight forward, and my face slammed into the steel-hard slope as my feet whipped out from under me.

I instantly switched sports from mountaineering to luge. I rocketed downhill. I was falling fast in less than a second. As frozen time snapshotted into second two, I sped past the highway speed limit. Then there was a moment of even greater confusion and a hard yank on my groin that took my breath away.

I've hit something. It's going to be terrible.

Stillness. I wasn't moving any more. My face was pulsing with raw pain, either an injury or the freezer-heat of the ice surface pressed against my cheek. I rolled onto my back, which required a solid push with my sore right arm. There was still pressure in my groin, but it encircled my upper thighs, too. My harness. It was supporting my weight.

For the first minute I hung there, pressed against a 70-degree slope of verglas-covered stone, I had no idea where I was. I knew I was on a mountain but couldn't for the life of me remember which one, or who I was with, and certainly not why I was lying on a near-vertical ice rink with a few thousand feet of air beneath my feet.

The details came back when a climber placed his hand on my shoulder.

"Phil. Stay put," he said.

Ang. Ang was his name. We were climbing together. A famous mountain. Everest. No, something like Everest.

I thought of the mountain, tried to remember what mountain I was on – I could recall the day's events clearly now – but the name still escaped me. How annoying.

A rope extended above me. It disappeared over a lip of stone. Our rope mate had to be up there. Ivan saved our lives.

I tried to call his name but it came out garbled. I raised a hand to my mouth, fearing I'd discover a smashed ruin where my lips had once been. But everything felt normal. I just couldn't make my tongue and mouth form words properly. Maybe I had a concussion. At least I wasn't shivering anymore, although I didn't feel any warmer.

Ang's hand rested on my shoulder. I tried to tell him I smashed my face but it came out as nonsense.

"It too steep," he responded. "Quicker if I climb up and we pull you. Try stamp feet, make muscle with arms to keep warm."

The instructions made no sense to me so I didn't follow them. Ice and snow dropped into my hood and a little down my neck as Ang chopped his way uphill. It felt like he was taking a really long time. I was looking up when he went over the lip of rock.

Ages passed. The Triassic became Jurassic. Maybe they left me. Dead weight. It was just the kind of thing they'd do. Ivan never did like me and Ang only cared about his son.

I couldn't feel my arms or my legs. I wanted to yell for help, or maybe just yell a curse at my former teammates. My mouth wasn't working right. Did I crack my head or something? I raised one of my arms and managed to pat my helmet with a mitten. I couldn't feel anything unusual and there was no blood on the mitten.

Chunk chunk chunk. The sound of crampons being kicked into ice. I looked up in time to get a face full of snow shavings. I spluttered and spit to rid my mouth of the frozen shards.

"You know what I like about you?"

The voice. It was him. My pretend fiend. I stopped trying to clear my goggles. I didn't want to see.

"You've got a plan," said the voice.

I wanted to say that I didn't have a plan. On the contrary, I was a man without a plan. All I had was vague intentions and the money to hire people with plans.

"Most of the climbers who come to this mountain want to live; they'll flirt with death but have no intention of finding it. A few are suicidal without realizing it. They lie to themselves and say they're living life to the fullest, but truthfully life terrifies them, so they come here subconsciously hoping to die. But you, well, I can tell you're something special."

My vision cleared. The speaker was right beside me, his face – if that was the right word for it – peering at me from less than a foot.

I'd decided on a name. There was a picture lodged in my brain, a nineteenth-century serigraph of some hideous, rotting being lurking over a prostrate woman. The cover of a book I'd never read: The Feast of Blood...

...Varney the Vampire.

Cold kills smell. Too bad I wasn't made of ice. I wondered if the stench was his body odour or his breath. It was the fetid odor of vegetation reduced to sticky liquid then fermented in coffin liquor.

The mouth contracted and expanded, a round wound lined with transparent needle-fangs. I was spared looking into its eyes – they were concealed behind a set of opaque ski goggles.

"I also appreciate what you've done," it said. "I'm thrilled Ivan and Ang have returned."

Who are you? The three words came out as gibberish.

"Your best friend. Better than best friends. Soul mates. You'll see."

His gloved hand reached toward me. A weight rested for a moment on my helmet. Then the hand retreated. The gesture hadn't felt like friendship. It was something else, something more formal. The opposite of a baptism.

The splitting sound of an ice axe being planted and the chunk of crampons climbing away. The sound grew faint above me. Still I hung in my harness. I yelled, a fit of frustration and pain, an incoherent yodel with just one intention: frighten my climbing partners into doing something, anything, except leaving me stranded where I was.

It worked. At least, it was only a matter of a few seconds after I stopped that the rope gave a tug to my harness and my whole body rose half a foot.

I started crying. I don't know why. I certainly didn't want Ivan or Ang to see. I just felt terrible in every way possible. My head was pounding, like my brain was three sizes too big for my skull. My toes and fingers burned and my chest felt empty and cold, a lifeless drum. My mind screamed hate at everything: the madness overwhelming me, the climbing partners who'd left me alone with my splitting psyche, and the ridiculous universe, too vast to even make sense. I felt elemental, like grains of carbon.

I didn't know how I'd hide my despair. A glimpse of me a moment before I came into view would have revealed a man in full panic, but a quick gulp of air and a wipe of my cheeks and I was just a tired climber ready for a cup of tea.

Ivan helped me pull a leg up over the lip while Ang stood back hauling on the pulley he'd jury-rigged with a spare rope and three carabiners.

"Get on up here, Phil," said Ivan, letting go of my leg to grab a fistful of my backpack strap.

"A ba," I said. "A ba doe wah."

Ivan frowned.

"Yeah, you're not making any sense," he said. "Are you cold, Phil? Ang, let's get a hypowrap going. He's freezing."

The sherpa laid out a ground sheet on the narrow strip of level ground on which we rested. Under it he'd placed a snaking length of paracord. On top of it went a sleeping pad, then a mummy bag. Ivan helped me get in the bag. Then Ang ran the remainder of the paracord up through the loops that emerged from under each side of the ground sheet and the two of them sewed the ingredients of the makeshift survival burrito shut. No more than five minutes and I was swaddled like Luke in a butchered Tauntaun.

Ivan asked Ang to put some water on.

"Might as well have a meal and refill while we wait. It'll be an hour at least before he's warmed up."

I must have drifted off to sleep. When I became aware of my surroundings again the stove was packed away. Ivan was on his sat phone, plugging his other ear to keep out the noise of the wind. Ang was hunched beside me, smoking a cigarette.

All of the sherpas smoked. People in Asia smoke more than Westerners generally, but mountaineers are predisposed to tobacco. Not sure why that is. I suppose if your life plan includes summiting 8,000 metre peaks, longevity may not be your priority. I'd read that smoking might reduce incidences of Acute Mountain Sickness. I suppose in every sport there are athletes looking for a possible edge, regardless of what it does to their long-term health.

I waited until Ivan ended his phone call to speak.

"Hey," I called.

Ang looked at me, then elbowed Ivan.

"You're awake," said Ivan. I could barely hear him over the wind. I nodded.

"You good to climb down?" he asked.

This time I shook my head. "Up," I said.

I was surprised by how little it took to convince him. I suppose we were a lot closer to Two than One, as long as I could move on my own steam, and the less time I was outside the better.

Ang packed away the hypowrap while Ivan clipped me onto a short rope.

"The next time I ask if you're cold, you tell me the truth, got that?" said Ivan.

"Yeah."

"No, not 'yeah'. How about, 'Sorry I was a dumbass and endangered every-one'? The only reason we're not all dead is that I'm incredible and lucky. I managed to throw a loop of rope around a rock that happened to hold when you dropped your full weight and Ang's on it. Calls don't get closer, Phil. You can't self-arrest on this shit. I don't plan on dying with you, okay. You get so much as a nippy nose, I want to hear about it. Got it?"

"Yes, I've got it. I'm sorry," I said. "Next time I'll speak up."

Ivan clapped me on the shoulder.

"Excellent. Now let's get up the chimney and settled at Two. Tomorrow it's gonna snow more and the wind isn't letting up. A shit day for you to meet the Black Pyramid, so perfect prep for the summit.

CHAPTER SIXTEEN

JULY 19

SNOW BURIED US at Camp Two. Ivan was up every couple of hours to shovel. I offered to take a turn but he shot me down. He wanted to make sure I was fully recovered from hypothermia for our push up to three.

There were no panic attacks in the chimney. Despite a core temperature marginally above popsicle, I'd managed a better performance going up that technical feature than I did the first time. Familiarity made a huge difference, and my body was getting used to hard days at altitude. By the time we'd arrived at Two I was feeling alive and energized. I'd babbled through supper. Ivan was fine with it. Said little but kept smiling.

Ang was off in his own world. He left for his tent – Ivan and I shared the other – before a second cup of coffee was even poured.

I emerged from shelter in the morning to three feet of fresh snow.

"Morning Phil!" Dawa said.

The youngest member of our team had his head poked out of the tent he shared with Ang.

"Morning," I answered. "You climbing with us today?"

"With you, Phil! I am your climbing partner today."

This came as a surprise, and not an entirely welcome one. The Black Pyramid would be the toughest sustained climbing of the whole ascent. I wanted Ivan with me.

My mentor explained over porridge.

"—But that's exactly why you'll be with Dawa. He's our best climber by far."

I raised an eyebrow.

"Look, he needs more experience guiding and I'll be right there," said Ivan. "And he really is the best on rock we have. He's done 5.14b in Yosemite, not to mention the Eiger Nordwand in a day."

It was strange to think of this young sherpa chilling out in Yosemite, or climbing routes that landed lucrative sponsorships. Was it racist of me that I assumed he was some kind of Asian country bumpkin, basically a mountain hick? Probably. Turned out even the most junior member of our team – not counting me, of course – was a prodigy.

The small size of our party should have been a big enough hint. Putting climbers on top of an eight-thousander usually involves a lot of bodies lower down the mountain. Typical commercial expeditions have lots of hired climbers to haul gear and fix ropes. Taking full packs, fuel and tents up and down the mountain is exhausting. Our small crew of sherpas were doing huge vertical, day after day, just so a dilettante – me – would have fixed ropes to climb safely. If many hands make light work, few hands require a world-class climbing effort. We could only run an expedition so lean with a top-notch team.

Ang started fifteen minutes ahead of us. He moved with the speed of a snow leopard and didn't bother using the fixed line. By the time Dawa connected me with two carabiners to the rope, I'd lost sight of our sirdar.

"This seven-millimetre fixed line is bomber," said Ivan. "Dawa is gonna be just an arm's length in front of you the whole way and I'll be ahead making sure the route is obvious and safe. Your job isn't easy but it *is* simple: stay calm and work hard. Can you do that?"

I nodded. He made it sound so straightforward. Do X and Y will happen. But not even Ivan the Terrible could take uncertainty out of an environment this extreme. The previous day I'd almost frozen to death, came close to sliding down the mountain, and hallucinated a monster – and those were just things that went wrong with *me*. Add objective hazards like rockfall, avalanches, crevasses and sudden storms, and you quickly realized no amount of expertise could make this endeavour less than very difficult and very dangerous.

Dawa placed a hand on my shoulder.

"I'll take care of you, Phil," he said. "We'll go slow. Just like the climbing gym but with fresh air."

I should have realized he'd spent some time in the States. His English was the strongest of all the sherpas. He even had a bit of a surfer-dude accent.

"I'll just apologize right now for how useless I am," I offered.

Climbing the Black Pyramid with Dawa and Ivan was not unlike stepping onstage to play rhythm guitar for Jimmy Page. Terrifying, amazing, and completely undeserved.

The first rope length was scrambling more than climbing. The holds were big and obvious. It was steep. There was a twenty-foot section that exceeded eighty degrees.

"Does it ever get vertical?" I called to Dawa.

"Oh yes," he said, "much better than this, but still very easy."

Better. Very easy. I think Dawa's scale was a little different than mine. He was capable of sending a 5.14b route, which is basically Spiderman territory: holds the width of a nickel and not many of them.

I could see Ivan above us. Just before we reached the midpoint of the second rope-length he whistled down to Dawa and pointed at a rock. The sherpa nodded. When we reached Ivan's previous position – he'd continued on – Dawa pointed at a shelf of rock that was showing me its underside.

"Don't grab this. It's loose," he said.

When I climbed to the level of the stone, I could see why both guides warned me. It was an obvious place to grab with a hand or rest a foot. I would have taken a spill. A minor tumble had only a small risk of resulting in a real fall – I was safely clipped to the fixed rope – but it would invite injury, and it's always a bad idea to send thirty-pound rocks careening down mountainsides to slam into equipment and climbers below.

The grade was getting steeper, with sustained climbing in excess of seventy degrees. Some of the surface was rotten choss that crumbled when you tried to grip it, but most was solid black granite. The route the sherpas fixed followed terrain with something secure to grab or push off of every metre or so. We encountered freshly chipped ice steps, and jugs that had been uncovered from their snow blankets. Ivan's work.

The altitude was definitely affecting me. I was gasping for air, my lungs working like a leaky bellows. I felt like I could never quite catch up, always a full breath short of having enough. A few weeks earlier I would have taken that as a sign to slow down, maybe even give up. My fitness had improved, certainly, but the biggest change was probably my tolerance for misery. I was hurting but it was a hurt I could stretch out for hours without quitting.

I can't imagine how frustrating our pace was for Dawa. I knew I was going as fast as I could. An experienced rock climber back at the indoor gym used to say "Slow is steady and steady is fast." I'm sure the sherpa thought I was testing out a new theory on K2: really slow is really steady and really steady is…just really slow.

Our first truly vertical section. It was a big rock protruding from the slope. There was a wide horizontal crack six feet up the surface and a thinner one just a metre lower. Dawa reached for the higher feature and found a grip immediately. He planted the front points of one crampon in the lower, hairline split and a moment later disappeared over the boulder.

This is easy, I reassured myself. And it really was, if you forgot about the thousands of feet of yawning space beneath you. Eyes front, focus on the rock.

"You're different."

The voice startled me. I jumped, which caused me to trip.

For an endless moment my knees and hips wobbled back and forth seeking balance. Adrenaline exploded in my stomach and head. A rush of white noise screamed danger. My flailing left hand finally found the granite surface in front of me and equilibrium was restored.

Varney had returned. The climbing partner that couldn't really be there but somehow felt a shade more real than anything else in the bizarre realm to which I'd condemned myself.

His clothing was period-accurate for a century earlier. Hobnailed boots and an ice axe long enough to use as a walking stick; jodhpurs and leggings, a heavy wool sweater with a wool blazer over top, leather mitts and a fur hat with ear flaps tied under the chin.

"I wonder if it's the lump in your brain," it said.

The apparition was standing right where I needed to stand to climb the boulder. I couldn't see Dawa but he couldn't be more than a few feet out of sight above me.

"You can *see* me," it said. "Not a flicker of movement out of the corner of an eye, or a shimmer in a wobble of sunshine. My full, manifested beauty. Most have to wait until the end. How lucky you are."

Very lucky. I tried to clear my throat and coughed.

"Could you just back off?" I said. "I'm not taking one step closer to you and I need to be where you're standing."

It might be make-believe, but Varney gave me the creeps.

He made a sound. I knew it was laughter but it sounded nothing like a noise you'd want at a celebration. It was the squeak and wail of abused bagpipes, the faint echo of claws scrabbling in a vast, underground chamber. Not a chuckle that conjured piñatas and punch.

The thing stepped back. I moved forward. I remembered what Ivan had said about the third man, and how it would show up when you'd moved far beyond the limits of normal physical exertion and mental strain. That wasn't how I was feeling, though. I felt pretty good other than the sensation in my lungs of trying to outrun Eliud Kipchoge with a plastic bag cinched over my head. I wasn't physically desperate or mentally distraught, and the being's presence wasn't an aura or shadow, or a vague sense of being in the company of a benevolent presence.

Varney was tangible. He looked like meat, the face almost lewd in its puffy, textured detail.

I found the grip on the boulder Dawa had used, a jug that inspired confidence even wearing bulky gloves. I looked down to my right foot as I wiggled a crampon point into the crack at waist height. I didn't look at Varney.

You're not real. Go away.

I repeated the words three times in my head as I scrambled over the boulder back into Dawa's company. The sherpa had a puzzled smile.

"Trouble? I heard you say something and you took a long time," he said.

"Even longer than usual?"

He laughed at my joke. The smile I returned was fake, a cover for the nausea rising in my throat.

Varney had followed me.

He was standing right behind Dawa. A drip of clear lubricant – or was it venom? – stretched out of the fanged mouth, pulled free and spattered down on the sherpa's shoulder. I could see the circle of wet; it had relief, like a penny-sized mound of slime.

"I like the name you've given me," he, it, said.

I didn't know if I was supposed to thank him.

"Oh, we don't need to be that formal, Phil."

Dawa traversed left under an overhanging rock. The footing was treacherous, gravel-sized stones glued in place with verglas. I hugged the overhang and sidestepped in Dawa's invisible path. I was finally getting more comfortable with crampons on rock. The first few days on the mountain the metal felt like skates. Clumsiness cured itself by necessity.

Varney came behind, swinging his ice axe back and forth beneath him like a pendulum.

"You're not like the other climbers," said the creature.

Let me guess, I'm fatter and less capable.

"That's true, but that's not what's significant," it said. "You're the first person to come here wanting life but seeking death. It's a delicious combination."

I had hoped coming to K2 would spare me from psycho-analysis – the heart-to-hearts, the doubt, the what-ifs. I wanted to fill my mind with action, not thought.

Contemplating life while preparing for death struck me as possibly the most unpleasant thing a person could do. Some people think there's no better way to spend your final moments on Earth, as if a few hours of coffee and conversation can wrap up the decades in a tidy little comprehensible package. I understand the desire for closure, the need for understanding, but I know myself too well to think it suits me. Contemplation leads to questions and questions lead to regrets. If there are people who can write an executive summary then smile as their heart stutters and stops, I'm jealous. No matter how hard I tried to make sense of my time alive, I knew my final thought would be the same: "Wait, wait, not yet, not yet dammit...!"

At its core the deal life offers is pretty basic. You appear, you do things, the time runs out, and you're done. Most of what you did dies with you. The few artifacts remaining will vanish in a generation or two, give or take a few thousand years. The entire species will vaporize itself or be reduced to sub-atomic particles by robots, or be swallowed by the sun. Next week or a billion years from now, memory will fail and all will be forgotten.

Dwelling on it – talking and thinking about it – won't change the outcome. Yet here I was, my own ego producing an icky climbing partner to say smug shit while I tried to forge ahead with an exceptionally vigorous death process. Wanting life but seeking death? What does that even mean?

The spectre laughed again. The sound felt like a punch in the stomach. I had to learn what amused this apparition and avoid thinking it.

Dawa kept climbing so I kept climbing. Varney walked beside me, hopping from stone to stone with the confidence of a mountain goat. It was infuriating.

Another near-vertical pitch. This one continued out of sight.

"Okay, so I want you to pace yourself here," said Dawa. We'd found a relatively flat spot to pause, an eight-inch-wide rock shelf where the sherpas had fixed the top of one rope and anchored the bottom of the next.

"I will go whatever speed you go, yes?" he continued. "It's steep for almost the entire rope length, so take breaks. Let me know, though, if you need a belay. Don't rest on the fixed rope if you don't need to."

That sounded pretty terrifying all around. I asked Dawa if there were any spots to catch a breath on the pitch.

"Sure," he said. "Two places, I think."

Two places on a rope fifty metres long. Christ.

"Bad choice," said Varney. "I'm pretty sure the miracle-working Son of God never existed. I can perform a few magic tricks, though. My favourite is crushing hope into despair."

The creature reached out its bare, white hands – the mitts were gone, revealing hooked claws like a cat – and placed the palms on Dawa's cheeks.

The reaction was instant. Not a flinch like you'd expect from a sudden touch, but a hissing intake of air. The sherpa swayed back. I raised my hands to stop him in case he kept going. He reversed direction and slumped toward the wall, turning his torso so his shoulder made contact with the ice.

His face was white. It matched the hands that held it.

Varney lifted his palms away from the sherpa's cheeks a second later. He stared at his hands then raised them towards me. A circle of red filled each.

"This – this is wonderful!" he said. "I wished for tears but instead received a wondrous gift of blood. What a surprise! Phil, you must be my good luck charm."

Dawa looked like he was on death's door and my imaginary friend was delighted.

"I need Ivan," Dawa rasped. "Please help me."

The mountain and the rope were real. So was the sherpa's distress and the danger I was in without him. Get help.

"I'm going for Ivan. Just don't do anything," I said.

I used a six-millimetre cordelette and fashioned a prussic above Dawa's ascender on the fixed rope. The easily-fashioned knot can be slowly moved up and down another rope, but any sudden pull – like a fall – would cause it to tighten. I clipped onto the line with a carabiner. Only then did I remove my own ascender from the fixed rope.

I leaned into the young man. I thought I'd see punctures in his cheeks where blood was drawn but the circles on his cheeks looked blue, not red.

"Be right back," I said. "Hang on, okay? I'll be one minute."

I clipped my ascender above Dawa's, then unclipped from the added security of the prussic. Speed was the priority.

"You don't need to save him," said Varney.

The apparition was right at my shoulder, like the tiny perched devil in the cartoons all grown up.

"Tell me to kill him," he said. "Let his life pay for your safe passage a little higher up the mountain."

I wondered what would happen if I swung my ice axe into the being's messed-up looking face.

"Why don't we find out, Phil," it said. "I'm curious, too."

I didn't do that. I squeezed the sherpa's shoulder instead.

"Okay, I'm going," I told him. Dawa looked like he'd been run through with a bayonet. I didn't know if he was even conscious.

How far ahead would Ivan be? Surely he'd be on the same pitch? I reached my gloved hand high up the ice-clad rock in front of us and skated my fingers along until I found what felt like a secure grip. I raised my right foot and took a couple of kicks at the ice. A satisfying spray of crystals pattered off my gaiters. I pulled with my hand and pushed with my toes.

I was twenty feet above Dawa before I ran so completely out of air I had to stop and splutter for two minutes just to catch my breath. I looked down. Varney stood beside Dawa. The creature waved.

It was another hundred feet of climbing before I caught sight of the rope's end. Ivan stood there, waiting. My hands were gassed. My calves were shaking with effort. I started yelling – screaming, actually, desperation tinged with hysteria – getting the guide's attention immediately.

I still hadn't come across the spots Dawa said were good resting points. I took the ice screw suspended from my harness and buried it in a clear blue lump beside me. Then I used a spare carabiner and my final length of cord to clip into the anchor. Two points of protection – I stayed attached to the fixed rope – are better than one.

Ivan reached me moments later. He'd rapped down the fixed line, no doubts in his mind about its security.

"What's up? Where's Dawa?" he said.

"Below," was all I managed to gasp out.

"Hurt?"

I nodded.

"Not dead?"

I shook my head.

"You good to come with me?" he asked.

I shook my head again. I was too tired to move and too tired to look at Varney again.

Ivan told me to make my way back down to the bottom of the pitch on my own time. He dropped out of view. I was another ten minutes sitting in my harness before my courage and strength were recovered enough to down-climb.

Ivan had the sherpa sitting on the eight-inch ledge. There was no sign of Varney.

The guide had removed his summit pack and was using it as a holster for the sherpa's legs. The young man's butt perched on the narrow lip and his feet were in the bottom of the slim pack, which Ivan had attached to the wall with rope and an ice screw.

"Says he's feeling better," said Ivan when I arrived, "but he looks like garbage."

The youngster's face was waxy but less pale than it had been.

"Not as bad as he was," I said.

"Really?" Ivan responded. "Well, I don't know what happened. Might have been a stroke."

"At nineteen?" I'd never heard of such a thing.

"It happens," said Ivan. "And it's hard to predict who it could happen to. Being fit or having altitude experience doesn't guarantee anything. Regardless, he needs to get down the hill fast."

Dawa was listening, of course.

"No, no. I'm feeling better," he started.

"Bull," said Ivan. "You look like crap. We're going down."

Dawa shook his head.

"Tsering will help me," said the sherpa. "You go on."

His brother, Tsering, was expected at Camp Three by the end of the day, coming up in a single push from One. We were only a few hundred metres above Two. If Dawa really was feeling better, it wouldn't be such a big deal for his brother to meet him and help him back down.

"I don't want you taking any chances," I said.

I was the client, the man who paid the bills. If I insisted on the three of us descending together, it would happen. But I didn't want to do that.

Despite everything, I wanted to climb higher. Every step up the mountain was difficult. I wanted the effort to count. Turning around at that point would barely improve my acclimatization. I'd fought through a waking nightmare to get to that point. And if Varney wasn't just a third man – if he was an apparition brought on by my growing tumour – every day mattered. I wanted Dawa to be safe, absolutely, but I couldn't be sentimental about it. If Tsering could reach him quickly, he'd be in good hands.

"It's not taking a chance," the sherpa answered. "I'm really feeling better. I could continue to Three."

"You're not going to Three," said Ivan. He reached under Dawa's knee and started digging in the top pocket of the climbing pack. His hand came out with the sat phone.

"I don't like this," Ivan said to me.

"It's his decision," I offered lamely.

The guide frowned as he punched at the keypad.

"It's not his decision, it's my decision," he said. "And I don't like this."

"We can go down. No problem," I said.

He didn't reply as he held the phone to his ear.

"Tsering, it's Ivan, over – your brother, over – he's okay, but needs a hand back to Camp Two, over – on the Black Pyramid, where are you? over – okay – yeah, third pitch, over – okay."

Ivan pressed the button to end the call and put the phone in a jacket pocket.

"Your brother is coming," he said to Dawa. "He's above the chimney. Shouldn't be long."

The sherpa nodded.

"I'll be okay," said the young man. "I feel good."

"We can stay if you need us," said Ivan.

A last chance. If Dawa said yes, that would be it. We'd turn around with the brothers and go back down to Two. Timing was everything. We couldn't wait and then still push uphill. The Black Pyramid would only get more dangerous as it warmed in the afternoon sun: stones fall from the ice, bonds holding snow together weaken.

"You have to go," said Dawa. "I'm fine. Really. I don't know what happened."

Ivan clapped a hand on his shoulder.

"Go back to Base and tell Raymond you need to be checked out by a medic from one of the other teams. We'll pay them. I want to be very clear about this – Dawa, listen – you don't come back up this hill until you've been seen, got it? Not even ABC. It could be nothing or it could be everything. You'll be paid, regardless."

I nodded and smiled at the sherpa.

"Take care of yourself," I said. He frowned.

"I'm sorry," he said.

"Don't be," I replied.

Ivan checked my ascender, then the carabiners and rope that attached my harness to it. The guide worked in an environment fraught with risk but mitigated the danger any way he could.

He looked up the mountain and then at me.

"I want to move fast," he said. "Today will be the hardest day of your life."

"Didn't you say something like that the first time we came up the chimney?"

My smile had no effect on his flat expression. One of his men was hurt. It was the wrong time for humour.

"If you're not in shape now to get to Camp Three," said Ivan, "there's no point in us being on this mountain."

CHAPTER SEVENTEEN

JULY 19

THE SUN HAD just vanished behind the mountains when the Camp Three tents came into view. The final part of the day's effort was an interminable trudge up a steep snow slope. Ivan told me the snow would continue up to high camp.

Snow is exhausting but also comforting. There's danger – concealed crevasses, entire slopes letting go – but it's hidden. Out of sight, out of mind. We could have been on a vast tobogganing hill for all the apparent jeopardy.

The camp was carved out of the slope, a long platform wide enough to accommodate two-man tents. I shared one with Ivan – our usual arrangement – and Ang was with Nawang. The head sherpa was outside when we arrived.

"Tsering call. Dawa good. Camp Two tonight, down to ABC tomorrow," he said.

Ivan nodded.

"He looked really bad," he said. "I don't want him on the hill again until he's checked out."

Ang handed me a Nalgene filled with water. I hadn't realized how thirsty I was until I took my first sip. Then I drained most of the one-litre bottle.

The Black Pyramid had been staggeringly difficult, requiring my complete concentration the entire time we were climbing. I'd never given birth to a baby (surprise!) but I wondered if the residual impression was anything like climbing the pyramid: it was inconceivable you had emerged from it intact and you never wanted to go through it again.

The monotony of the snow slope had given me too much time to think. I tried to be mindful, like the daytime television gurus talked about, but how could I focus on breathing when the memory of Varney's foul breath kept intruding? I couldn't get the apparition out of my head. Why that companion, why that specific hallucination?

What did his awfulness say about me?

I felt guilty. It was absurd, of course. I didn't cause Dawa's medical condition. Still, it was my apparition that hexed the poor youngster. I wanted to tell Ivan about the phantom attack, the bleeding palms and the moment when the sherpa was struck down. I tried to figure out the timeline, how my hallucination could have coincided with the sherpa's collapse.

The answer was almost as disturbing as the visions: it probably didn't. The order of events must have gotten muddled in my crippled brain. Chronology was slipping.

I didn't want to give Ivan evidence I had deteriorated further. I stayed silent.

We ate supper in pairs. I was a guest in the sherpa tent. Nawang cooked for me while Ivan and Ang used our tent. I tried to converse with Nawang but his English was the worst of the team. I think he was the oldest of the sherpas. It was hard to tell with any of them. Dawa was the only one who looked young. High altitude, sun and wind had tanned their wrinkled faces into dark leather.

If any climbers on K2 were Ivan's physical equals, it was the sherpas. Nawang was the shortest of the party, barely five feet tall. Even with his undersized stature, though, he exuded power. He wasn't slim like the others. His profile was blocky, legs bowed. His hands were corded with sinew. Even his face was muscular, little nuggets balling and flexing in his cheeks when he smiled or chewed.

"I really appreciate your hard work," I said between sips of soup.

Nawang smiled but made no attempt to volley the seed of conversation back to me.

The soup was good. Curry-something. Solid food was hard to stomach. This high up, the body directs blood to vital organs and the muscles you need to keep going. The gut is neglected, so appetite fades. Meanwhile, we were burning probably 6,000 calories each day. The end result was inevitable. I was losing weight. My ribs were visible and my hip bones protruded.

I looked like a cancer patient. Ha ha.

After supper I returned to my tent.

"I've spoken with Raymond. Dawa is done. It was probably a stroke. They're gonna see if he can fly out with a news team."

"A news team?"

"Journalists don't stay long," said Ivan. "Have to be on oxygen the whole time, so they cycle through almost daily. I thought they'd be bored by now, move on to something else. But the prospect of a rich guy croaking doing something nutty has broad appeal."

"Thanks," I said. "Do you think he'll be okay?"

"Should be. He's young. But he probably won't be able to climb," he said. "There's big money in expeditions. Climbers are celebrities in their villages. He might have to find something else to do and there's no way it will be as lucrative. Guiding is a powerful temptation: risk your life to change the fortunes of your family."

One night at Three and we descended. Going down the Black Pyramid was a lot less sketchy. I was finally comfortable with rappelling, so we made short work of the most difficult, technical sections. We reached Two in three hours, and Camp One a couple of hours after that. We were back at ABC by mid-afternoon.

Best of all, there was no sign of Varney.

Raymond prepared a feast. I had an appetite – stimulated with tumblers of whisky – so I took advantage and ate far too much. My stomach protruded as I limped off to the spacious tent I had all to myself.

The plan was simple. The summit called. A day of rest, then back up the hill the next time we had a weather window.

I was a mountaineer. Not an alpinist – I was short-roped or fixed-roped everywhere I went – but I was gonna lay claim to the title mountaineer, dammit. I tried to cobble together a formula in my head as I lay in my warm sleeping bag. Did a guided climb to Camp Three on K2 equal a solo ascent of a tough 11,000er back in Banff?

I could say it did. Why not? It was just me talking to me. The point was, I'd really done something. I'd had so many moments, potential turning points, where I could have walked away, but I didn't. I wasn't even at the top yet but I felt accomplished.

Okay, I was a bit tipsy. Five ounces of whisky was enough to make me warm and happy and just a little bit proud. At least I had the good sense not to brag in front of the others. The mental image made me snort: me boasting to Ivan and the sherpas about my climbing accomplishments.

Wind and freezing rain moved in overnight. I spent the day in my tent reading. I was on the second-last Harry Potter book and didn't have the final volume with me. I toyed with the idea of having *The Deathly Hallows* flown into Base Camp and carried up to ABC. I chuckled at the absurdity of the idea. Then I grinned at the thought of doing it on purpose just to give the news crews something ridiculous to report.

Rich people are despised. If you want to attract votes on election day, just promise to gouge the wealthy.

I didn't deserve my riches, but I don't think getting wealthy gambling on crypto-currencies was typical. Some millionaires inherit their cash, of course, but probably most pair good decisions with hard work and it pays off. Luck plays a big role, sure – a kid from Askole doesn't have the same opportunities as one from Ottawa – but that rationale for condemning prosperity could be used to disparage the large majority of people born in a wealthy country like Canada.

So screw the haters. I didn't feel bad about what I was doing with my paltry millions. When I spent it, someone else got it. Ivan would decide what to do with his six million dollars. Ang would decide what to do with his quarter-million. Raymond would get a share, a rope merchant in Skardu got a piece. A tiny nugget of my gold would trickle down to a baggage handler in Islamabad's airport because I decided to die in Pakistan.

Flying in a copy of *Harry Potter and the Deathly Hallows* would have been a bit obscene, though, even for me.

Five days of snow followed, broken only by temperatures barely mild enough to bring rain. I asked Ivan if this was it, if the season was done. He said no.

"This is typical, Phil. We got lucky up 'til now. Crazy lucky. One season in twenty. And our luck is holding. Meteorology says there's a window coming end of this week."

We got our reports from overseas, a firm in Switzerland that did weather for a lot of the big guiding companies. The predictions so far had been rock solid.

"Three, maybe four clear days, but then a storm moves in," he continued. "We'll want to be back down before that hits. So we'll start in crappy weather and meet the good stuff hopefully by the time we're above Two."

We were talking in the mess tent. Ang wasn't around. I'd barely seen him. The other sherpas – Nawang and Tsering – were up on the hill caching equipment for the summit bid. They never left ABC with less than fifty pounds in their packs. Ivan had jotted down the supply pyramid for me on a white board before we'd even established Camp One. I didn't pay very close attention because it all boiled down to a simple concept: you needed a lot of stuff on the mountain to end up with a small amount of stuff where you needed it (Camp Four) on the night you needed it (the summit push). There's an alternative to our siege-style climbing: the alpinist lugs his or her own stuff up the hill. They also generally eschew things like fixed lines and oxygen.

Ivan and Ang climbed K2 alpine-style for the successful attempt on the ice face above the Bottleneck. They got their altitude training on Cho Oyu a thousand miles away in Nepal – a big mountain but vastly safer – then choppered in to Base Camp at K2 and knocked off the climbing feat of the century in a little over a week.

I may have become a mountaineer but I was not an alpinist. Constrained by the austere rules of that climbing style, I'd be at my limit trying to summit Mt. Robson, Banff's tallest peak. I was decades of experience away from being able to do the same on K2.

81

I had a million questions. I wanted to know what the Bottleneck would be like, if the traverse was scary, how difficult summit day was compared to the Black Pyramid. I wanted to know what we'd do if we got trapped high in a storm or if someone collapsed with pulmonary edema.

I knew the answers to some of those questions but that wasn't really the point. What I wanted was reassurance. This was the last big thing I hoped to accomplish, ever.

My fortune was a fluke. My marriage was a failure. I never had kids. So this was it. A tall piece of rock. I couldn't imagine failing, the hopelessness I could sense waiting to overwhelm me in defeat. The funny thing was, I couldn't imagine success either.

If Camp Three was the moon, the summit was Alpha Centauri. Somehow I needed to go the speed of light and all I had was a diseased, carbon vessel. I had to do the impossible. I didn't need to be reassured that I would survive. I just wanted to know we had a real shot. But I didn't ask and he didn't offer.

"Anything you drop or put on the ground will be gone," Ivan was saying. "You drop a glove, it's gone. You drop your ice axe, it's gone. So just don't. You're from a world where there's always a second chance and mistakes can be corrected. This is not that world. Up top, a mistake can kill, and I can't promise I'll be able to save you."

"I know," I said.

He held eye contact.

"I know, I know," I repeated. "Listen, I don't want to get all maudlin and shit, but I wanted to tell you, you and the rest of the guys –"

My speech was interrupted.

"Knock, knock," said a man already entering the mess tent.

He was tall, maybe my age, but much better looking. He was wearing a vest. That's what stood out to me: a tan-coloured safari vest that looked like it had just been pressed. His mountaineering boots looked brand new, too, and they were a light construction ill-suited to the abuse footwear receives on the Abruzzi.

"Hi, sorry, you must be Phil Truss?" he asked. He reached out a hand. I instinctively shook it.

"You from one of the other teams…?" I started.

Ivan stepped up beside me.

"He's not a climber," Ivan said to me.

I couldn't believe I didn't notice. As if the gear wasn't give-away enough, the man had a slim oxygen tank strapped to his back. He was holding a clear plastic mask down at his left side.

"No, I'm not," he said. He released my hand. "Robert Chapman. I'm with World Report. And you must be Ivan."

Ivan didn't accept the proffered handshake.

"Not giving interviews," said the guide.

I echoed my mentor: "Yeah, not giving interviews. How did you even get up here?"

Ivan moved towards the door and I followed.

"I have a guide," said the man. "Listen, I wonder if you could – I'd just like to – I wanted to talk to you, get your view."

We exited. Chapman followed. The man's guide was waiting outside, a slightly-built local in running shoes, jeans and an ancient Sun Ice jacket. He was having a conversation with Ang. Our sirdar's tone was definitely hostile.

"Honestly, I don't want to be a bother," the reporter started again. Ivan turned on him.

"Well you are. You don't belong here."

"Interesting," the man said. He smiled. I didn't like the smile. It looked like the grin of a man who's convinced he's more clever than the people around him.

"So I don't belong here," the reporter continued, "but he does?"

The reporter pointed at me. I wanted to punch him in the face.

"Ivan, you're a world-class climber," he continued, "and you've been bribed into carrying this novice to the outer limits of human achievement – to the very place that has defined your career. Ivan, have you sold out?"

World Report. I placed the name of the publication. It was a tabloid, one of those grocery checkout rags. I was quite impressed, really. They had actual reporters, not just fiction-writing hacks. He'd basically dismissed me as luggage, though, so I had no regrets about my next two words.

"Fuck you."

Chapman placed the mask up to his face. I'll hand it to him, he was willing to take a chance running down a story. The reporter would be in trouble fast if something went wrong with his oxygen rig. He'd be relying on us to save his ass.

"Devil's advocate, Phil," said Chapman. His breath hissed and echoed, shades of Darth Vader. "No judgment. I just want to hear the nuts and bolts of what you're doing. I need a story and I would think you'd want your perspective – your voice –

to be part of it. I came a long way to be here and rumour has it you're making a summit bid soon. A final chance to say farewell?"

Ang was watching. Then he was in motion. The sherpa covered the distance to the journalist in a blink.

"This is your chance say bye-bye," the sherpa said to Chapman.

The reporter extended his right hand. This, apparently, was the way he started every encounter with someone new, regardless of circumstances. Ang reached out his right hand like he was going to shake but then thrust his palm into the much taller man's chest. Chapman was forced to take a step back to catch his balance.

"That is assault," said the reporter. "This is not your land and I have permission to be here."

"You don't have permission," said Ang.

I looked at Ivan. Ivan was looking at our sirdar.

"I do have permission," said Chapman, "I have permission from the Ministry – "

Another blink and Ang's chest was an inch from the Westerner's, his head tilted back to look up almost a foot into his adversary's blue eyes.

"You don't have *my* permission," said the sherpa. "You leave now or I stab your soft belly, feed your stomach to birds."

Ang drew his climbing knife. It was kept in a neck sheath. The blade was less than three inches long but no doubt wicked-sharp; running it over a whetstone was like a daily meditation for the sherpa.

Chapman lowered his mask. His eyes bulged at Ivan and his voice shook as he spoke.

"Is this a joke? You can't do this. Tell him to stop."

Ivan's voice was calm and quiet.

"This isn't your place and you're not our people. I think he might really kill you."

The reporter's gaze searched wildly, finally fixing on his own guide – hoping perhaps the local would intervene – but the man was pointedly staring down at his running shoes. Chapman took a step back from Ang.

"I'm going straight to the police," he said.

"You should," Ivan replied. "We'll be on the Abruzzi if they're looking for us."

The reporter left. He barked something at his guide. The slightly-built man growled back. They'd have an unpleasant clamber back through the icefall.

"Did you see how scared he was?" I said.

Ang smiled but it didn't look friendly. His eyes were wild.

Ivan spoke: "They might not think it's so funny back in Islamabad, but whatever. The guy was a douche."

"Totally," I said.

Raymond feted us that night with roast lamb on wild rice, and a fresh-baked pie made with an unfamiliar berry. It was tart but I liked it. The meal was washed down with a honey-sweetened lassi. I went to bed stuffed, got up once during the night to pee, then opened my eyes, wide awake, the minute Ivan entered my tent early the next morning.

It was pitch dark and cold, his headlamp a piercing white star.

"Snow is falling and the wind is up," he said. "I want to get to Camp One before it's too bad."

"What time is it?"

"Just after two. We rope up in half an hour. Eat, have a shit, and let's move."

CHAPTER EIGHTEEN

JULY 27

THE CLIMB UP to Camp One was brutal. The wind, the snow, the cold. Ang left early so it was just Ivan and me. I kept expecting him to turn us back. When we paused for a break three hours into the climb, I had a moment of weakness.

"I can't do this, Ivan. It's a freakin' blizzard. You know I want this but it's too hard."

Ivan shook his head and yelled into my ear.

"That's crap. You either want this or it's too hard. Never both. So get it together. You made the rules. No retreat, remember?"

We made it to Camp One. Ang had tea waiting for us and water to refill our bottles. I downed two chocolate bars in the tent. I'd found my second wind. I felt energized as we roped up in a team of three and left the tents behind.

Another hour of climbing. I was surprised by how strong I felt. The storm was blowing hard but my legs had juice. I'd found a good rhythm for breathing. We followed the route of the fixed line but didn't lock onto it. There was twenty metres between us, Ang ahead and Ivan behind. Every rock surface was slippery, a thin sheath of ice cloaking any black and grey that wasn't buried in snow.

I wondered, not for the first time, if I was that much fitter than before or if my tolerance for pain had simply increased. My heart rate was very high but I felt like I could go on forever.

Two hours into our climb to the chimney the storm started to slacken. I noticed the gusts becoming infrequent. Then the ambient wind speed started dropping, too. Snow was still falling heavily but the temperature was rising.

The chimney looked as ominous as ever. Ang didn't even stop. He unclipped from our team rope when I reached the bottom of the face. He scrambled up the narrow gully with a single carabiner hooked onto the fixed line. It was reckless. If he slipped, the carabiner would keep him on the rope but do nothing to slow his fall.

You have to take chances on the mountain. Fixed ropes are a good example. They're great insurance for technical sections and provide a quick rappel route for descents. They do fail, though. Anchors come out. Ropes break. People make mistakes. It's about risk management. Fixed ropes are a considered risk. You block the what-ifs from your mind – to avoid being paralyzed with fear – and get on with the job.

Sending without any mechanism to slow a fall was just rash, though. I knew Ang was hurting – his son's illness obviously weighed heavily on his mind – but it still surprised me to see it compromise his climbing.

I waited for Ivan. I told him what Ang was doing.

"He's not himself," I concluded.

"You think?" Ivan said. "What was your first clue, when he threatened to murder a journalist in camp?"

I tried to undo my biners and transfer them to the chimney rope. Ivan pushed my hands away. He made the switch himself, leaning down and eyeballing my groin to make sure it was right.

"We need him, Phil," he said when he stood up. "This doesn't happen without him. Now up you get and no mistakes."

The chimney never got easy. My heart rate spiked even higher. Surely there was a simpler way? An entire mountainside and this was the route everyone took?

Ang was waiting for me at the top. So was Varney.

He was standing behind the sherpa, his formless chin resting on the shorter man's shoulder.

"Hey, you made it," said the apparition. "That rotting body of yours still has a spark.

You know, Phil, I'm not sure if it's your fear or your misery that's making me feel a century younger, but I'm glad you're here. Truly. I'm feeling stronger and more creative. And definitely hungrier. I swear I could eat the whole world."

I stared at the creature and Ang stared at me. I tried to smile at the sherpa, tried to pretend my skin wasn't crawling from the sound of Varney's alien voice, his ghoulish words, the look of his bulging eyes and fang-filled mouth. Why did I have to put up with this? Climbing K2 wasn't tough enough, I had to do it with my brain conjuring nasty hallucinations, too?

Ivan was ten minutes behind me. The apparition insisted on staying behind Ang, even as the sherpa moved. And he kept smiling, at least I think that's what the twist of the mouth hole was supposed to be. At one point the monster started singing, a droning noise that rose and fell, like a cross between a saxophone and a Hammond organ. Clunks and clicks were interspersed seemingly randomly in disharmonic scales. Each phrase ended in a guttural, hacking cough. I feared vomit would spew from the creature's aperture. When it didn't happen, far from being relieved, I just assumed he was working his way up to it, some spectacularly foul bile that would pollute the entire planet.

Ivan clambered into view atop the small boulder where the chimney exited. Varney stopped singing.

"There's no way you see the top of this mountain, Phil," said the being. "But I'm going to enjoy watching you try. I'll relish every morsel of effort, every portion of anguish. Keep marching to your death. Keep feeding me."

I stared at Varney. I couldn't help it. Ang scowled. He must have thought I was looking at him. As soon as Ivan reached my side, the sherpa turned away, leaving with a couple of terse words.

"He's yours."

The Nepali left. Varney went with him, still hunched over and resting his chin on the shorter man's shoulder, like some kind of fucked-up comedy routine.

Ivan and I roped up, fifty feet between us. Clear skies appeared just before we reached our destination. We arrived in Camp Two with the warmest temperatures we'd yet experienced on K2. I stripped off my shell, then my insulating mid-layer, just a thin layer of long-sleeved polypropylene underwear remaining to protect me from the blazing sunshine.

I half expected the creature to be there, skulking around camp, or still perching its hideous visage on the sherpa's shoulder. Ang was alone when he came out of the sherpa tent, however, and I was spared hallucinations the rest of the night.

"Camp Three tomorrow, Phil," Ivan said later as we lay in the dark tent we shared, anticipating sleep. "Summit in two days. I can't wait to show you. It's magnificent."

I stayed awake a long time. I tried to imagine seeing the Bottleneck with my own eyes, not in YouTube videos or photos in books. I tried to picture what the actual summit would look like. I knew there was no final, technical piece of rock to overcome, just the top of a really big hill. What would it feel like to be in that place? It felt impossible that it could happen.

Then I wondered if that was how it would feel when death finally came for me: impossible to imagine, impossible to accept. And yet it would claim me, in the same way I would claim the summit if I continued forward. Of the two, death and the summit, only the former was assured but both felt inevitable lying there in the dark. Certain yet inconceivable.

I imagined Varney's face in the dark. I saw his face when my eyes were closed. A grotesque, leering distortion of human features. The third man was supposed to help me wasn't it? Give me strength when I thought I had nothing left? Apparently my cancerous brain was giving me a diseased companion, a phantasm to drain me of hope and aspiration. Instead of helping, Varney seemed bent on soiling a dying man's only ambition.

I wouldn't give up. My mind might try to smother me in fear but I knew something it apparently didn't: You can't get worse than dead. Darkness was coming for me regardless. The only light was uphill.

CHAPTER NINETEEN

JULY 28

WE STARTED UP the Black Pyramid early in the morning, hoping the extreme cold would reduce rockfall. Rocks still fell, however, a steady rain of gravel occasionally punctuated by fist-sized stones. One struck Ivan in the helmet. It must not have fallen from very far or it would have had a bigger effect. The guide grunted once, shook his head, and kept climbing.

Ice gradually claimed my extremities. The heat of the previous afternoon had vanished. It wasn't cold like the hypothermia I'd experienced before – my core stayed reasonably warm – but my digits burned worse, then went numb. Perhaps my body had learned to draw life-sustaining fire into my centre at the expense of luxuries like fingers and toes.

I kept discovering new levels of fatigue. As I fumbled up the vertical jigsaw of the pyramid, I tried to remember the energy and enthusiasm I'd experienced briefly the previous day. How could it just abandon me? And how could I feel this horrible, still press on, and still think I would have energy at Camp Four to set out for the summit?

Keep moving. I don't know how many times I repeated those two words in my head as I climbed. If I had a gram of energy stored in my muscles, I could still get half an inch closer to the top. You'll only stop when you stop.

We didn't rest during our climb of the pyramid. I asked once. Ivan answered with a curt no. I snatched bites of chocolate in the rare moments when he was pausing to assess his next foot placement. I gulped almost a litre of water while he repaired an anchor that had broken loose. I never saw him consume anything. Men like Ivan don't need mere food and drink, not when there's a job to do.

I understood the need for speed. Speed is safety in the mountains, especially in exposed terrain. If an avalanche hit while we were on the face, there was no chance we were getting out of the way. You were either protected by a fortunate outcrop of rock or you died. And you never knew when the next stone might be a basketball instead of a fist. Twenty pounds of rock from almost any height meant broken limbs or skulls.

My lungs gasped. My heart stuttered. Many hours after we left Camp Two we pulled ourselves out onto a steep snowfield.

Ivan finally stopped. He pointed a hundred yards to our left, where our two tents were still picketed on a narrow snow shelf carved from the slope. A necessary location, not a safe one. Hopefully we'd only have one or two nights there – one on the way up and, if we didn't have the energy to bypass it on the way down, one on our return.

You couldn't see the shoulder or the summit, either. The snow slope rose above us like a wall to blue space. If I didn't know better, I'd think we were almost to the top.

I climbed into our tent while Ivan stopped to talk with Ang at the sherpa's shelter. As I struggled to get into my sleeping bag, I found myself mumbling a prayer: Please don't visit, please don't visit. Just let me have tomorrow. Let me see the shoulder and look up at the summit, without another visit from Varney.

I'd studied the photos, had a copy of a favourite back at Base Camp: a shot of the summit cone from Camp Four on a clear day. The ice serac shone like polished vinyl. The Bottleneck appeared short, and the summit squatted above the ice face. The proportions were wrong, a result of foreshortening, but it didn't matter. It was a picture of sacred ground; a real, physical space that was imbued, even for Phil the atheist, with mystical properties. A place where humans could not tread yet somehow did.

Just let me see it. Let me have Camp Four. Let the real light waves from the real summit enter my eyes. Let me touch it that way at least. If I achieve nothing else, I'll die happy.

My prayer was answered. If I was visited by Tumour Varney, it was only in forgotten dreams. I slept well and woke feeling genuinely rested, as unexpected as it was welcome. Good sleep was hard to come by above twenty-thousand feet.

In Camp Three I was as high as I'd ever been on the mountain. We'd be reaching new heights when we started up the snow slope after breakfast. I didn't care that sherpas had paved my path right up to the Shoulder, or that fixed ropes placed by someone else would secure me through the Bottleneck and the traverse beyond. I wasn't competing with other people.

We traveled in our usual three-man rope team, Ivan in front and Ang at the rear. The guide zig-zagged his way up the steep incline. At each switchback, I transferred my ice axe to the uphill hand, and made sure the rope attaching us stayed uphill as well; both measures were to assist in smoothly transitioning to a self-arrest position if I slipped. There were no lines fixed between Three and Four. You were expected to use your ice axe to stop if you fell. The right hand would drive the pick into the snow, while the left hand steadied the haft. You had to keep your weight on the axe head for maximum effect. Crampons could help if you were quick, but if you started sliding, then tried to arrest by digging in your feet, the result could be a snapped leg.

My thoughts were occupied with avalanches. I wasn't really worried about slipping. Crevasses didn't even cross my mind.

Our route up the Abruzzi had been blessedly free of yawning chasms. We'd skirted numerous large crevasses between Base and ABC, and a few small ones between ABC and the chimney, too, but there'd always been a way around.

We were just under an hour into our climb when a crevasse revealed itself ahead. I'd grown used to hopping over small fissures on the hike to Concordia and from there up to K2. Two feet, three feet. But usually from level terrain to level terrain. This crevasse was on a steep incline. The far side, just over a metre away, was higher than where we stood by almost two feet. There was no realistic way to get a running start at it, and my thirty-pound pack would have slowed any attempt at sprinting anyway.

Ivan is tall. He walked up to the edge and launched his right foot forward, landing cleanly on the other side and continuing on his way.

I am short. And I'm not Ivan.

I should have spoken up. It wouldn't have been hard to secure the crossing. It would have meant admitting frailty, however. On our summit push I feared that any display of weakness might be grounds for Ivan to turn us around. I wouldn't do it – I wouldn't turn around – but worst case, it might result in a confrontation. If Ivan left me and took Ang with him, I'd have to push on alone.

Me and Varney. A truly terrifying prospect.

I was stupid. I saw the ease with which Ivan crossed and decided to copy him. I launched my right foot forward. It didn't rise to the higher elevation. My foot struck the face of the crevasse a full foot lower than the rim. The crampons didn't stick. Instead, the snow wall collapsed, taking my foot with it. I swung my ice axe, hoping to hook the pick into secure ground. I succeeded – the axe found purchase – but my hand slipped down and off the end of it. So I fell.

I fell just long enough for my brain to register I was in free-fall before I stopped.

My helmet bounced off the wall of ice in front of me. My harness yanked on my crotch and compressed my abdomen. My body immediately took over. Adrenaline flooded my brain and raced through my torso. Air huffed and puffed out of my chest three times per second, trying to inflate me with the oxygen I'd need to wrestle cave bears or punch a sabre-toothed tiger.

I looked up at the sky, the edge of the crevasse twenty feet above me. The stick-shape of my axe handle was silhouetted against the blue sky. I was okay. I was going to be okay. If I stopped falling, it meant my partners stopped me. My climbing team was the best on any mountain, anywhere. They'd have me out in a jiff. I just needed to sit tight.

A minute passed. I focused on slowing my breathing. Two more minutes.

"Hello?" I called. I strained to hear an answer.

Nothing.

I counted to sixty, then continued to one hundred. I wondered how long I could hang there before my brain summoned company. I didn't want to hear that alien voice or see that wound of a face.

I looked down into the crevasse, a rich glassy blue that narrowed into black. Another fifty feet and the walls closed in enough to catch me, squeeze me, make me their own. I imagined the horror I would feel if I saw movement down there, long claws extending out of the darkness, or round, glowing eyes bulging up at me.

"You good?"

I looked up. The silhouette of a man beside my axe. Ivan.

"Yeah, just taking a break." I tried to make my voice sound relaxed. I doubt I succeeded.

"I'm going to feed a rope down to you in a second, okay?"

A carabiner on the end of a line descended to my outstretched hand. When it reached me, I clipped it to my harness. I immediately felt better. I was still haunted by the mental image of Varney clambering up from the shadows below – or even, in defiance of gravity, sliding towards me on his belly – but I resisted the urge to look down again.

Don't feed fear.

The rope pulled on my harness. I rose half a foot.

I could picture what Ivan had rigged up top. Once he'd stopped my fall by self-arresting with his ice axe, he would have scraped away snow until he reached a good ice surface and then sunk a screw into it. Only then would he have started to set up the ropes he needed to create a mechanical advantage that allowed him to easily haul me out of the crevasse.

People are heavy. They're even heavier with backpacks. There's also a surprising amount of drag on a rope when it's loaded. That's where setting up pulleys comes in handy. Take enough time and use enough rope and carabiners, and you can make it as easy as you wish. Mind you, knowing Ivan, he could have scaled into the crevasse, thrown me over his shoulder and hauled me out fireman style.

I stopped moving. I was only a few feet below the downhill lip of the crevasse. My breathing had slowed. I was actually starting to appreciate the break from activity. I'd need to come up with a joke to tell at supper, something about how Ivan should have left me another hour so I could rest up.

Did I feel it before I heard it? That was the only way to explain the speed of my reaction. I was already in motion when I was able to actually categorize the sound: it was the rasp of prehistoric talons scraping stone bones, and it came from under my feet, from the midnight place close beneath me.

My hands scrabbled uselessly at the sheer ice as I screamed, "Ivan. Jesus, Ivan!" I couldn't look down. I wouldn't.

Another stuttering scratch echoed up the ice walls. Sound waves thrown by a bone cleaver as it butchered the forever-buried.

"Get me the fuck out of here, Ivan!" I shouted.

I could feel the pull of doom daring me to drop my gaze and peer into the deep. Black hole gravity compelled me. See your end, Phil. Watch it approach.

My head tipped forward, my eyes frantically trying to stay pinned upwards even as my chin pointed further and further down. I don't want to look, I don't want to!

The harness squeezed my pelvis and I rose two more feet, then one more. I looked up and extended a hand towards my axe. I grabbed it like a talisman, St. George grasping the pommel of his sword just before the dragon lumbered into sight. Then I swung my left leg up over the rim and rolled onto the surface.

From my prone position I could see Ang waiting downhill on the far side of the crevasse. Shame mixed with relief. How useless he must have thought I was.

"You okay?" asked Ivan.

I couldn't summon words. I barely managed a nod. Ivan turned his back and continued trudging uphill. I clambered upright and followed.

We encountered more crevasses. One beast was twenty feet across, spanned by a snow bridge. Ivan never slowed. I changed the grip on my ice axe as he crossed, preparing to drop to the ground in an arrest position. The bridge held.

My turn. I tried to keep my brain blank, with little success. Surely I wouldn't fall in a crevasse twice in one day, twice in one hour? The bridge narrowed to a metre at the middle. It felt rail-thin. I held my breath as I crossed the centre of the span. I stepped softly, like I could somehow diminish my bodyweight if I just imagined I was a pixie.

The bridge held.

Ang crossed safely. We walked another hour. It was getting warmer. The breeze was steady with no strong gusts. Then the summit of the mountain came into view.

I almost couldn't believe it when I saw the first white point. We kept climbing and more was revealed. The point became a broad pyramid. Then the ice of the huge, overhanging glacier. My heart sped up when the base of the serac was revealed. There's the top of the Bottleneck and the traverse!

Fear and exhilaration pumped in my veins. Even a climber as experienced as Ivan was affected. He stopped. I stopped. After a minute he called over his shoulder.

"This is my favourite place, Phil. I'd stay forever if I could."

"Me too," I answered.

I looked back at Ang and pointed at the summit. He nodded in response.

The Shoulder was less steep than the snowfield but we'd also been rapidly increasing our altitude. Our exertion level wouldn't drop much as we pushed to Camp Four. Ivan called a break.

"I want to get as high up the Shoulder as we can," he said, "leaving a bit of distance from the Bottleneck in case a serac drops. The higher we get today, the less we need to climb tomorrow."

Tomorrow. I knew that was the schedule but it still triggered a twist in my bowels.

Tomorrow we would summit. And tomorrow wasn't even tomorrow. I knew the plan. We'd make Camp Four before dark, sleep a few hours – if we could – and then head up by midnight. Tomorrow wasn't a day away, it was less than twelve hours.

I wanted to tell Ivan I was scared. Would the admission be a relief or just give more substance to my fear? I said nothing.

"You good?" he asked Ang.

"Good," said the sherpa.

"You good?" he asked me.

I nodded. He smiled. Ivan had a good smile. It didn't show up often, which made it more valuable when it did.

"I gotta tell you, walking in from Askole, I thought you had zero chance of getting this high," he said. "I figured we'd get you to Camp One – *maybe* – before you turned back. You've done a good job, Phil. You should be very proud of what you've achieved here."

I squinted for effect.

"That almost sounds like a compliment," I said. "That wasn't a compliment, was it?"

"Nah. I don't give compliments to assholes," he answered, still smiling.

CHAPTER TWENTY

JULY 29

DARKNESS. A CLINK of metal and a murmur of voices. I thought of a spoon stirring sugar in a cup of milky tea. Karen's voice in a sun-drenched living room. I was with her, she was with me.

Then I noticed the sharp cold as I turned my head. My face emerged from a sleeping bag into the night.

I didn't know where I was.

A glow passed across a surface a foot from my face. A tent wall. A headlamp outside. I was camping. Karen was just here, I was sure of it. I could still hear her voice.

A deep cough startled me.

"It's time," said a male voice in my ear.

Someone was lying right beside me. A shrouded figure pressed against my body. Too big, not her. What was happening?

"It's time, Phil," it said again. "Let's get moving." Now the figure rose, loomed over me. I heard the mechanical bbrrrzzz of a zipper opening. My eyes adjusted. There was more than one headlamp outside the tent. People were moving. The sounds of preparation.

I asked the only question.

"Where am I?"

The person in the tent's entrance – a man with a calm voice and a stuffed nose – stopped moving.

"Camp Four, Phil. We're climbing to the top of K2 today."

Planet Earth shifted an inch and I remembered.

We're on a mountain. I chose to be here. I will be dead soon.

"Start moving, partner," said the man. Ivan, that was his name. My guide.

The zipper opened. Ivan stepped through the open hatch. Arctic air rushed in and filled the space he'd occupied. The zipper was pulled back into place.

"Ang will be by with coffee," he said from outside. "You were up a little while ago. Did you get back to sleep? It's eleven. I want to start by midnight."

I assumed he was talking to me. I couldn't see him. He hadn't turned on his headlamp. I mashed my hands into my face and rubbed.

I knew my confusion wasn't just fatigue or altitude. *You're too late*, I said to the tumour in my head, *you can have me tomorrow but today I win*. The headache had subsided. It was there when I went to sleep but now I had to search to find it. Go figure. Climb to an altitude where everyone's head hurts and mine somehow felt better.

Summit day. The most lethal day in the whole lethal endeavour. I'd climbed to twenty-six thousand feet, give or take. Just two thousand more.

My boots were in the sleeping bag with me. I started a dance with my feet, trying by feel to find the right one for each. I'd slept in my one-piece down suit. My gloves hung from the sleeves, attached to each other by a string that ran through the suit. I was a toddler again.

I panted from the effort to shove my left foot into the wrong boot. The air was a lie. Each lungful contained less than a third of the oxygen it would supply at sea level. I tried to imagine the effort the day would take. Thankfully, I was interrupted.

"Phil? It's wake time. I have tea for you."

Ang unzipped the tent. He was wearing a headlamp, too, but expertly avoided shining it directly in my face.

"But I drink coffee."

The absurdity of my complaint reached my brain after the words had left my mouth.

"Tea is better for you today," Ang said.

The sherpa's attitude seemed to have improved. Less worried about his son, perhaps, or just caught up in game day.

"It is good day for try," said the sherpa. "One day in thousand. No wind. Very lucky."

I asked Ang if he got any sleep. He shook his head and asked me the same.

"I think so," I answered. Karen felt so real yet I couldn't put my finger on a single concrete detail from my dream.

"You drink tea. The three of us, we will stand on top today, I promise," he said.

The sherpa backed out of the tent. I managed to drink the tea without spilling. When we set up the tent in the daylight the wind had threatened to tear it loose. Outside was silent now, except for the sound of gear being adjusted and teammates murmuring last minute plans.

There were three teams at Camp Four. Ours was the smallest, of course, just Ang, Ivan and me. Our sherpas stocked the high camp more than a week earlier and then headed down. The Spanish were there and also the Italians. The latter had a large team. Their high-altitude porters, HAPs, left at sunset to fix rope up the Bottleneck and across the traverse to the final, steep snowfields that led to the top.

Italy was the first country to put climbers on the summit of K2. Lacedelli and Compagnoni stood atop the mountain July 31st, 1954, only a little more than a year after Norgay and Hillary achieved their feat. And just as Everest was considered "Britain's" peak in the minds of colonial mountaineers, K2 belonged to Italy.

Ivan had given their team money for access to the fixed lines. No one could have stopped us from pirating use of the ropes but the death zone was the wrong place for ill will.

We'd have one chance at this. If I couldn't summit my first try, success on a second attempt was very unlikely, especially given that I'd probably be trying it solo. Neither of my companions owed me two shots at the top. Above eight thousand metres, bodies break down and recovery from physical effort is all but impossible. We were getting weaker every hour.

The tea was finished. Breakfast wasn't happening. My appetite had been relatively decent all along but extreme altitude had finally killed it. My body was working too hard keeping me alive to waste blood and energy on digestion.

I laced up my boots, then wrestled them into the overboots. I had to pause before finishing the job. My hands were freezing. I stuffed my bare fingers into my down suit. My circulation was sluggish. Dehydration thickens the blood. I'd get frostbite if I wasn't careful.

Maurice Herzog lost all his fingers climbing Annapurna. He lived the rest of his days with paddle hands but reportedly had no regrets. I didn't relish the prospect of losing my fingers, but I understood the deal he made. Mind you, if *I* lost digits, I wouldn't have to live with that shortcoming as long as he did: Maurice got ninety-three years, four decades more than me.

"It's quarter to twelve, Phil. Time to go."

I grunted in reply to Ivan's disembodied voice. I fished my one-litre bottle of water out of my sleeping bag – kept there to prevent it from freezing – and dropped it into the light summit pack I'd carry to the top. There wasn't much else in it. A chocolate bar I'd never eat and an extra pair of gloves in case I somehow managed to lose my tethered mittens. Ang had my camera.

Ivan was outside the tent.

"No, don't even take a step. Not until your crampons are on," he warned.

"Yes, Mom."

The guide bent over and secured the spikes to the bottom of my boots. Then he held my harness for me. I braced my hands on his shoulders as he strapped it around my waist, then secured the leg webbing. He pulled the waistband tight, then attached two carabiners to the loop over my pelvis. He snapped a looped knot into the carabiners, then checked the metal clasps were locked shut. No mistakes on summit day.

The knot he'd clipped into my harness ran three metres to his own. In addition to being clipped onto the fixed line, he was short-roping me the whole way to the top. An unusual choice. We'd argued about it before bedtime. I said it would slow us down and put him at risk. I pointed out how ludicrous it was endangering him for my sake. But he didn't budge.

Ivan was talking.

"...olamide and dexamethasone in Ang's pack, so you tell me if you start feeling really out of it."

Injections in case I was struck with altitude sickness.

"So, more out of it than I usually am?" I said.

He frowned.

"I'm serious, Phil. You want to help the team, you keep yourself safe. Don't put me in the position of having to decide whether or not to abandon you up there. When this is over, you can find a crevasse back at Base Camp and jump in for all I care. But today is going to be an uneventful stroll into the stratosphere."

I nodded.

"Just remember. I'm not going back down without touching the top," I said.

It was his turn to nod.

"It's not the kind of thing you forget," he said.

I wondered if Varney would be joining us today. I thought he'd be waiting outside the tent, standing behind my guide, or following Ang as he crossed the slope from the Italian tents back to us.

"Ropes should be good," said our sirdar. "Storm move in day after tomorrow. Good today. Winds fifteen."

"Cold, though," said Ivan.

Nights were never warm at Camp Four, of course, but I could tell by the scratch of the air on my exposed cheeks the temperature was minus 30, maybe lower. It the wind came up, it would be lethal.

Summit attempts always leave at night. Two reasons for that. The first was simply that it takes a long time to make it to the top and back, and it's better to deal with night on the front-end when you're fresh, than after you've already struggled to the top of the mountain and you're depleted. Camping higher on the mountain could hypothetically shorten summit day. But the Shoulder was the best site on K2, and a higher camp would mean more material dragged uphill and even poorer recuperation prospects.

The other reason for a night departure was the usual: cold keeps ice and rocks frozen in place. Only on this day, the threat of falling objects was magnitudes bigger. A serac calving off the overhanging glacier above our summit route – the same ice face Ivan free-soloed – wiped out ropes in the infamous 2008 tragedy, stranding climbers above the Bottleneck.

The Bottleneck. I couldn't see it in the dark. I couldn't see anything not spotlighted by a headlamp.

I knew our route as well as a person could know a place they'd never been. I'd watched countless YouTube videos, as well as the handful of documentaries chronicling climbs and mishaps on the Pakistani peak. The least technical way to access the upper reaches of the mountain was to ascend the Bottleneck.

Least technical doesn't mean *not* technical, nor does it mean safe. The ice-coated couloir was hundreds of feet tall, rising steeply from the top of the shoulder to the foot of the massive, overhanging glacier Ivan had climbed.

The glacier regularly dropped chunks of ice the size of buses into the funnel below. Remember that really hard level in that really hard video game you played as a child? Yeah, like that. Or just imagine the life of a bowling pin.

Once we ascended to the top of the gully, we'd still have to traverse to the left a couple of hundred yards, exposed to ice and rock fall the whole time.

The traverse was steep. The Bottleneck was steep. Everything was steep. A 45-degree slope feels almost vertical when you're a novice climber. Sections of our route would be 80 degrees and blue ice.

The traverse complete, all that would remain was hour after hour of slogging up the summit snowfields. Very steep. Could be buried in hip-deep snow. Get to the top – dehydrated, starving, hypoxic and frostbitten – and we'd still have to climb back down. I was fatalistic about that part. Summit K2, and then what would be, would be.

"You ready for this?" Ivan said to me.

"No," I answered, "but I'm still going."

We were the first team to leave, if you ignored the hard work of the HAPs. I could see headlamps shining inside the Italian tents, and the Spanish tents, too. It was amazing how a few flimsy fabric walls could look so inviting when you're casting off into the void.

I turned my back on life's frontier and shone my headlamp on Ivan's boots as he crunched uphill. Ang wasn't roped up with us yet – we'd form a single team

100

once we were past the traverse's fixed ropes – but I could hear the sherpa's boots crunching through the icy crust of the snow behind me.

The conditions were perfect. If the surface was harder, a single slip might carry you off the mountain. Much softer and we'd be wading through deep snow. Ivan was setting an easy pace for me. That was why we'd left before the others: all that time on the hill and I was still slow. The guide said he wanted us to complete the round trip in less than 24 hours, which would have us almost down the Bottleneck before full dark returned.

It was quiet. The loudest noise was the crunch of crampons, except when Ivan coughed. Ang's feet were the only part of him that made a sound. His words as we got ready to leave Camp Four were the most I'd heard from him in days.

There was nothing to see. The air was still, the darkness absolute. Just little circles of light, with snow and metal and brightly-coloured mountain apparel. We were taking three breaths for each step. Our pace would drop drastically on the upper slopes.

I didn't know how long we'd been walking when I noticed Varney had joined us. I felt a presence on my right, just beyond the light. Then he came closer. And closer still. Right beside me, an intimate distance that made me want to push him back.

"You're too close," I said.

"What?" Ivan called over his shoulder.

"Nothing. It's nothing, sorry," I said to the guide. I looked sideways at Varney. He smiled with the long, see-through fangs of those nightmare fish that dwell in perpetual darkness. The odor of rotting plants filled my nostrils despite the deadening effect of the frigid air. And those bulging, spider eyes. Only two of those, thank god. A full set of eight might have sent me screaming down the hill.

"You'll probably have a heart attack – or a stroke," said the wraith.

I'm going to die regardless, I said in my head, might as well try to get to the top of this mountain.

"Kind of a shame, really," said Varney. "I've enjoyed you."

Sorry, can't say the feeling's mutual.

"You can't hurt my feelings," it answered. "On the contrary, your dread and hatred are gratifying. Not as satisfying as the crimson treat you helped me draw from that youngster. Shame he made it off the mountain. I can't help but wonder, though, what a *larger* meal would feel like."

I didn't help you, I said, conversing with my own imagination.

"Oh you most certainly did. I've never had that strength before. You were the difference. Even now, walking beside you, I can feel energy filling my empty chest."

I scowled at Varney

"Come now, don't deny me," it continued. "It's a little thing I ask. Pick one, Ivan or Ang. A quick swing of the axe and the deed is done. And perhaps this time you can partake."

Not gonna happen, I said.

"You can take comfort in knowing I'll get them anyway," he said.

Fucked up, ugly, nasty shit in my head. I was getting ready to die, my tumour was to blame, yet it couldn't leave me alone for a final walk.

Varney's inhuman mouth drooped, kept drooping into an impossible frown. He was wearing crampons but they made no sound. His down suit was unzipped, the arms tied around his waist. A thin, long-sleeved thermal t-shirt covered his torso. His helmet fit strangely – it rested too high, like the dome of his skull wasn't a dome at all but something sharp.

"Let me leave it with you," he said. "And it doesn't have to be with the axe. I'm open to any method of murder you prefer. You can even ask me to do it for you. I'd relish the challenge."

He wasn't at my side anymore. He stood above Ivan, illuminated in a headlamp. A single pale Varney hand hovered over the guide's head. The hooked talons looked like black metal.

"Say the words," said Varney.

Don't. Don't do it, I said.

Maybe I could have banished the vision by pushing it to do the impossible, forcing my brain to confront its own fantasy. Illusions can't actually behead people.

Chalk my reticence up to superstition. Unease about the intersection of my fantasies and the very real damage Dawa suffered on the Black Pyramid. Committing imaginary murder felt like bad mojo.

Varney looked at me, his arm still raised. What would I see if that claw dropped? Nothing, of course. Hallucinations don't kill. Yet it was so easy to picture the way Ivan's body would slump, to imagine the sound his helmet would make as it cracked into the snow.

The being's mouth formed a circle, teeth projecting around all 360 degrees. I could see his purple tongue lashing in its red cavity. His words hooted and creaked as he spat them out.

102

"Resolve withers, Phil. The body loses strength and the mind follows. And everyone has a weakness. You'll see."

The claw lowered. Varney stepped out of the circle of light. I could still just make out his silhouette, though. The darkness of night was passing. I could distinguish the shape of Ivan against the white of the hillside, see the blackness of the summit cone up ahead.

I looked for the creature again but he was gone.

"Flat patch here. We'll take water," said Ivan.

I lodged the pick of my axe in the slope, giving it a pull to make sure it was secure. Anything casually placed on the ground would follow the laws of gravity and plummet to the glacier-filled valley 10,000 feet below us.

The water was good. Funny how gulping water can take the edge off fatigue. You're taking in less air because you have to swallow, yet the net result is improved recovery. Weird.

"How are we doing?" I asked Ivan. I looked over at Ang. He leaned into his axe with both hands, staring at the sharp butt where it met the hard snow. Another day at work.

"Fine so far," said the Ukrainian. "How are you feeling?"

I nodded. Too tired to ask why water makes you less tired.

The light revealed the mountain above us. We'd almost reached the foot of the Bottleneck. I could see a team of HAPs starting down the couloir. They'd be exhausted after spending the night attaching ropes all the way up through the traverse.

It was barely five minutes when Ivan said he wanted to go. My heart was still pounding. I panted, trying to fill my lungs. Details sprang out from the slopes above as sunlight flooded the mountainside. The summit looked so close, just peaking over the battlement of ice that overhung the Bottleneck, protecting the summit from all but the bravest or stupidest supplicants.

We met the first of the descending HAPs. Ivan stopped to talk. I took the opportunity to gulp extra air. I looked back. Ang was using the end of his axe to tap snow out of his crampons. I could see the other parties behind us. Two rope teams and, further back, a third. Nine climbers in all. I recognized a brown down suit in the team bringing up the rear – one of the South American women. The closer clusters had to be the Italians.

Ivan bumped fists with a Pakistani rope fixer and we started plodding upwards again. We weren't switchbacking. There was no time to zigzag, even though it would lessen the approach angle. Speed was safety in the exposed couloir. I walked with my toes splayed out, a technique French alpinists call canard. The Bottleneck looked less steep close up.

The massive overhanging glacier was still terrifying, however.

I wasted enough breath to blurt out a sentence: "You climbed that?"

Ivan didn't respond.

The ice face was a hundred or more vertical metres of green-blue glass. Where it wasn't smooth it was cracked into individual seracs, widowmakers waiting to drop. I looked up the chute we were about to ascend and tried to imagine what I'd do if an iceberg let go and dropped into the gully. Die, I supposed.

We reached the fixed rope. I hooked my ascender onto the line and attached a cord to it from my harness. The ascender's metal handle should have been foolproof: load the device and it gripped the rope. It worked whether you were pulling yourself uphill or taking a break while you decided if that tightness in your chest was a myocardial infarction. People still managed to kill themselves using ascenders and fixed ropes, though. Fatigue and oxygen deprivation make you stupid.

"Pay attention, Phil," said Ivan. "Place your feet where I place mine. Same with your axe. You're not going to tumble, not unless I'm going with you, but there's nothing anyone can do to stop ice or rock fall. If something comes down the Bottleneck, get behind a rock if you can. We're moving fast – that's how we stay safe in this shooting gallery – so hustle and don't water-ski on the short-rope. Ang, you good?"

"You talk too much. Let's go," said the sherpa.

Ivan smiled.

"Okay," said the guide. "We rest when I say we rest. Otherwise don't stop."

He turned to face the ice slope, then looked back.

"And don't unhook for anyone. They can unhook when they want to pass you. No exceptions."

I nodded.

Ivan set a brisk pace. He rarely needed to change his foot or axe placement, his instincts honed over two decades on some of the planet's most dangerous terrain. We were up on our toe spikes almost immediately. I'd set the pick of my axe with my right hand and use the left to pull on the ascender. I didn't touch the short-rope. If I was going the right speed – not too slow or fast – it would drape between us properly without adjustment.

My whole torso shook with the effort. A fresh bath of sweat warmed my body despite the cold. I didn't look to the sides and I didn't look any further up than Ivan.

I definitely didn't look down. I'm pretty good with heights – and being in the Bottleneck felt less exposed than lower down, on the Black Pyramid – but I was laser-focused on mastering the little piece of the planet within arm's reach.

Ivan stopped. He unhooked his ascender and reached to the right with his axe to plant his pick off the trail. Then he kicked his crampons in the same direction and moved off the fixed line. A steady spray of ice shards hit me in the face; Ivan must have been blocking them the whole time. Looking up I could see more of the HAPs descending. I reached for my ascender, uncertain what to do. I started to twist the lock on the carabiner that attached the safety cord running from my harness to the metal handle. Ivan saw my hand and guessed what I was doing.

"What the fuck did I tell you, Phil? Do not leave the fixed line."

I let go of the carabiner. I looked down at Ang. He had also removed his ascender and moved over. I supposed passing one climber – me – was easier than passing three.

The first of the descending HAPs reached me.

"Move over," he said.

Ivan spoke for me: "Can't do it."

"You have to move over," said the rope fixer.

I shook my head.

The man swore in a foreign language. You didn't need to know the words to understand the sentiment. He unhooked from the fixed line – a fixed line he might have placed – and kicked and chopped his way past me on the left.

"You should not be on this mountain," he spat as he passed.

I didn't make eye contact as the next HAP unlocked from the fixed line and descended past me in the Bottleneck. It was odd that shame still affected me. With the end so near, I thought I'd reach some higher plane of consciousness, an ethereal being consumed with thoughts of the universe and causation. But no. Still embarrassed.

"Just stay put, Phil," Ivan called down to me.

The sunlight flashed off the glacier overhead. It was bright even with sunglasses. Without eye protection you'd be snow-blind in a few hours. It's happened to climbers on K2. During the 2008 tragedy, a climber wound up descending the wrong way and spent more than a day blindly inching his way down sheer rock faces just hoping he'd get somewhere better, lower than where he'd been.

He was one of the lucky ones. He lived.

105

Two more HAPs passed, then finally the last one. He was the youngest. I vaguely recognized him. I ventured a smile when he kicked down to a position parallel to my own. His expression was more sneer than smile.

"You're in the wrong place," he said.

I felt a flare of anger and responded.

"Your buddy already said that. Thanks, though."

He gave me the middle finger with his left hand. I looked away and looked up. A boulder the size of a dishwasher was soaring down from heaven.

It was too late to do anything. It was going to hit me.

Except it didn't. It made a direct strike on the unroped HAP who'd just flipped me off. He vanished, like a kangaroo that's stepped in front of an Australian road train. He was instantly gone, vaporized. What remained was a red smear carpeting the couloir all the way down to where the fixed ropes began.

"Jesus, Jesus, Jesus," I gasped.

I didn't know if other people were yelling. I didn't know if sound even worked anymore. It was just me locked in my head for a split second.

I was pulled from my paralysis by a low chuckle. Hugging the ice chute on my right side was Varney.

"It worked!" he said. "A gorgeous display. Look at how the red glimmers in the sunlight."

You're not real, I said to him.

"Are you sure? I feel real. That rock was pretty real. I've always been able to give a loose piton a final wiggle, or cause a worn crampon strap to finally break. But that stone was solid, wedged into the ice face, and now it's a thousand feet lower and coated in gristle. A perfect bullseye dropped from above."

I looked up and found Ivan's gaze.

"Should we help?" I yelled up to the guide. I looked down to Ang to see if he had an opinion. He didn't look shocked. For a moment it struck me how utterly morbid high-altitude mountaineering was. The sherpa had seen this before, or something much like it, maybe many times. Death stalked everyone here.

"We can go down any time you want," said Ivan, "but there won't be any point. That guy's gone."

Gone. He wouldn't be gone if he hadn't moved off the rope. The boulder would have missed him by a couple of feet at least. It was my fault.

"Yes," said Varney. His artificial voice, vocal cords made of splintered chicken bones or a throat lined with charred wood.

"You killed that boy," said the creature. "I couldn't have done it without you. Your midlife crisis has its first body. Only that's not quite right, is it? It's an end-life crisis and the victim isn't a body anymore. More like scarlet gravy. No need to get hung up on specifics, though. I'm happy for both of us, regardless."

Please shut up, I said.

"Let's keep moving, Phil," Ivan said. "Ang, we're going double-time. Get the hell out of this couloir."

I snapped the pick of my axe into the ice above my head and pulled. I followed with my left hand, then gripped the ascender as I lifted my right foot and kicked my crampons into the hard surface. After repeating the maneuver three times I was gasping for air. I sat back into my harness, the safety cord locking me to the fixed rope. I looked down. Ang was only twenty feet behind me. The Spanish rope team had stopped at the bottom of the couloir. Both Italian teams were in the chute and pushing hard.

The HAPs were almost to the boulder and the scant remains of their colleague. None of the foreign climbers had gone back. Some distant part of me wondered if that was wrong but I didn't give it any energy. I had none to spare. Even guilt for my role in the accident was muted, a low murmur that would never be given full voice, not if these were my final hours.

Death was normal. Life was the anomaly. A brief flash of mingling atoms, then back to our eternal state.

"Oh, it's not quite like that," said Varney. I thought the voice was beside me but then realized he was ahead. He sat perched on a sharp rock outcropping. His long-sleeved shirt was gone, revealing a bare chest that was ruined, smashed, like a turkey carcass denuded of flesh.

"Life eternal is real, Phil," he said, "and you don't have to be good to have it."

Ivan pulled even with Varney.

"I'm going to use you, Phil," said the phantom. "I'm going to breathe your pain and savour your torment. You will nourish me, and I will hurt you. And maybe, just maybe, you'll come to love it."

The apparition jumped to its feet. Effortlessly he leapt over Ivan to another jagged rock ten metres further uphill, then to another. In thirty seconds he was out of sight.

I'd been motionless the whole time. My heart rate was back down to 130.

You are bullshit, Varney. You are my cancer and I defy you.

I pulled my right spikes free of the ice face and raised my foot. Fear will not stop me. My body will not stop me.

My brain will not stop me.

I swung my foot back then kicked forward. My crampons snapped into the chute a foot higher than their previous placement.

Was Varney really fruit of the lump in my brain, or just a hallucination brought on by oxygen deprivation? Maybe I was just boring old crazy, suffering a mental breakdown due to strain and deprivation.

I wouldn't have to keep it together for much longer. A few awful hours. That thought raised my spirits. I felt the smallest flicker of happiness. I was in a horrible, beautiful place, doing a magnificent, terrible thing.

We think we're in control but it's an illusion. We pick from the tiny number of options we're presented, and even that choice is a result of Newtonian forces pushing one chemical ahead of another in the pudding between our ears. Maybe the smashed HAP a thousand feet below had a brain tumour growing in *his* head.

Maybe being squashed like a bug was a mercy.

"Almost there," said Ang. The words barely reached me. It sounded like he was talking to himself.

The wind picked up. Clouds obscured the sun. The temperature dropped instantly. My extremities felt better, though. I'd avoided frostbite so far. I remembered a story Ang told me at ABC. A sherpa apprentice lost his mittens during a push to establish Camp Three on Everest and didn't have a spare pair of gloves. Ang had an extra pair, of course, but embarrassment kept the youngster from saying anything. By the time the eighteen-year-old sherpa gathered the courage to ask his mentor for help, two of his fingers on his left hand and the thumb on his right looked terrible. It didn't matter in the end. A serac collapsed on him in the Khumbu Icefall.

I pulled and kicked and pulled and kicked. My throat felt like it was on fire. The muscles in my lower back screamed. I grabbed onto the pain and tried to focus my attention on each protesting fiber. There was meaning to be found there – something profound in the agony and the effort – I just wasn't sure what it was

Ivan stopped.

"Take a break," he called down. "Five minutes."

I sat back on my harness. I clipped my ice axe onto my harness with a biner, and used my other hand to reach back to the water bottle in the mesh pocket of my pack. I drank deeply, consuming half a litre in a single pull. I heard the crunch of Ang's crampons below and looked down to see him eating an energy bar.

"Ugh. Don't know how you can eat those up here," I said.

I thought it would provoke a smile. Cold bars are hard and flavourless. He barely even noticed I'd spoken. He ate because it was fuel and he had a job to do.

I liked Ang early in the expedition but he'd been distant ever since the runner showed up in base camp with news about his son Nima. He was worried about him, obviously. I couldn't really relate. Parents love their offspring, and they should, but I'd never even had a pet hamster. Karen always said I was cold. I never denied it. When I did get emotional, a distant little part of myself sat back and judged, cynical even of my own feelings.

"How you doing?" Ivan called down.

It took a few seconds to gather the oxygen to respond.

"Good. Tired. But good," I yelled.

"We're almost there – the traverse," he said.

I nodded. The sun was back out. The temperature jumped ten degrees. I'd read about K2 expeditions climbing in T-shirts on summit day. That wasn't the case for us. The blazing sun would scorch cheeks and noses, but the temperature stayed solidly in the negative.

My guide kicked at the ice chute and placed his left crampons. Then he planted his ice tool with the swing of his right arm. I glanced down between my feet at Ang. He made eye contact, I was sure of it, but his expression didn't shift at all. He looked right through me.

It wasn't right. He wasn't right. I'd mention it to Ivan again if I got a chance. Maybe Ang had altitude sickness.

Altitude sickness can strike as low as 10,000 feet. The best way to prevent it is to increase elevation slowly. Your body's ability to adapt maxes out, however. And there is no acclimatization above eight thousand metres.

It was hard to predict who it would affect. A trained athlete might be struck down where a less fit individual wasn't. Previous success at height – an entire career spent in the mountains – was no guarantee of immunity. Pulmonary edema or cerebral edema were the most serious effects. Tissues swelled. The lungs filled with water or the brain pressed against the skull. Injections could slow the trauma but the only solution was to get low as quickly as possible. Getting sick above Camp Four would be a life-or-death situation.

Maybe it was nothing. He'd been faraway for days. His boy, all the press and bullshit. Perhaps the death of the HAP.

Fuck it. None of it mattered. I wasn't Ang's therapist. He was still climbing and looked about as tired as I'd be walking a dog down a city sidewalk.

I pulled with my ascender, then reached with my axe. Placed my left foot, then my right. Ivan had stopped moving. He'd unclipped and was shuffling to the left. I could see a horizontal rope extending that direction beneath the overhanging serac:

the fixed line that would take us to the final summit slopes. We'd reached the top of the Bottleneck.

I wanted to celebrate but didn't have the lung capacity. I whispered a hoarse cheer to myself. I looked down at Ang. Was it possible his expression was even more dour? I could see one of the Italian teams beneath him. They'd caught up a lot of ground. Less than half an hour behind us. Almost close enough to hear if I yelled down. The other Italian team was a little further back but the Spanish had turned around. I saw brightly coloured figures down on the Shoulder.

Ivan clipped into the new rope.

"Almost there, buddy," he called. We were so close his voice sounded conversational. "Keep coming. Stay on the fixed line. I'll clip you onto the traverse."

I wondered what the glacier hanging above me looked like without sunglasses. It had to be blinding. What did Ivan think the first time he was here? He didn't make a left onto the traverse that time. His route was straight up the glacier's vertical face, wending his way through precariously balanced seracs, a climb many elite mountaineers later dismissed as suicidal. At the top of the Bottleneck, after all that effort to get so high on such a massive mountain, his real challenge had just begun.

Maybe Ivan had no imagination. A vivid imagination might be deadly up here. So many ways to die and so few ways to survive. Or did he perform the old samurai trick and imagine he was already dead, a living corpse scaling an impossible route to the underworld? He never told me what he planned to do with all the money I was paying him. A man who wants that kind of dough can't hate life entirely.

"Lookin' good," said Ivan. I could almost reach his foot with my ice axe.

"Feeling good," I answered.

The guide looked down past me to Ang.

"How you doin'?" he asked the sherpa.

"It's okay."

I peered down. Ang looked bored.

"You feeling okay?" Ivan asked him.

"Gut no good. I climb though."

Those power bars were hard to eat at high altitude on a good stomach. Not sure why he was downing them if he felt rotten.

Ivan slapped my shoulder and waved me up. He was already clipped onto the traverse. Ivan took my ascender off the Bottleneck's fixed line and attached the cord to a carabiner on the traverse rope. We were good, as long as that rope stayed on the mountain.

The 2008 disaster on K2 happened not more than a hundred yards from where we rested. The climbers were descending in the dark and a serac broke loose from the overhanging ice face, wiping out the fixed line. One climber was immediately swept away. The others were stranded above the Bottleneck, in the dark, exhausted from their summit. The death toll hit double digits.

There was a precipitous drop on the left side of the traverse and a vertical ice wall on the right. Ivan stomped a path through the crust of the snowpack and tackled the route head on. I didn't have his confidence. I faced the mountain and shuffled sideways. There was a moment of terror every time I pulled my axe loose. Ang was walking forward across the face of the slope like Ivan but used the ice tool in his right hand to anchor his balance.

I stole a glance back to the top of the Bottleneck. The first of the Italians had reached the traverse.

"These guys will be faster," I panted to Ivan.

"Doesn't matter. They can overtake us after the traverse. Focus on your climb," he said.

Yes, focus on my climb. My calves were cramping. My shoulders were screaming. My temples were pounding. My lungs were on fire.

Why did dying have to be so hard?

CHAPTER TWENTY-ONE

JULY 30

THE TOES OF my left foot were going numb.

I looked down, as if somehow I'd see something other than a ten-thousand-foot plunge to the glacier below. My foot was encased in multiple layers: socks and a tough fabric bootie cover, then a leather and synthetic boot, over which was zipped a knee-high, waterproof, insulated layer – all of which was supposed to stop me from losing feeling in my tootsies.

It didn't matter. Not really. I wouldn't need toes where I was going.

The Italians were on the traverse rope behind us. One of them, their lead climber, said something to Ang. The sherpa didn't answer; he still looked bored.

"Keep up, Phil. At this speed we're not making the summit," Ivan said.

I was already higher than I'd ever thought possible. The summit was close. I suddenly felt certain that I would stand there, that I would make it to the top. I had to.

I wasn't sure why it mattered. It had something to do with purity or maybe perfection. It was a glorious end to my story. I loved the idea of forever being the man who climbed to his death atop the great summit. Once I was there, though? Once there was only sky above me? Well, I didn't know. That was the part that remained unscripted.

I'd lost the Jesus spark in my early teens. Life could be reduced to a man-sized heap of rocks, powders, fluids and smells. Consciousness was a little trickier, sure, but invoking God to explain the unexplainable just created a whole new set of problems.

Atheism had made sense for decades. Now, though, I found my resolve slipping.

The imminence of death makes any religious conversion suspect, of course. That whole thing about foxholes. It's not like I was about to start singing hymns or reciting the Lord's Prayer. There was one thing, though, that rattled my scientific certainty: reality is really weird.

Did you know time changes depending on the speed you travel? I'm not talking about losing four hours when you fly from Halifax to England, or gaining four when you land in Vancouver. I'm talking about actual time. Airline pilots are a tiny bit younger in age than their grounded peers because they spend their lives zooming through the air at high speed. Now why is that? *Because.*

Because that's how time works. Einstein and some other geniuses figured it out. Does it make sense? Not to me. Apparently the universe's rules are just laid out that way.

Gravity is another serious mind-fuck. It affects every second of our existence, but we have no explanation for it. It just *is*. Gravity would kill me if I jumped off the mountain and no one could explain why.

Is the notion there might be something waiting for me beyond death any stranger than, say, the existence of a black hole millions of times the mass of our sun spinning at seventy percent of the speed of light? I didn't think so.

It's not that I was suddenly confident in the existence of an afterlife. Not at all. Probably I'd just *stop*, a calculator stripped of its battery. But I wasn't certain anymore.

Quantum entanglement exists, dinosaurs roamed the Earth millions of years ago, and long after our sun dies life may just be starting somewhere else in the galaxy. We use these words. Time. Gravity. Galaxy. They're succinct, even simple. They allow us to be comfortable describing "things" that are far more bizarre and mystical than any spell I invoked as a kid playing Dungeons and Dragons.

Certainty was bullshit.

"Almost there, Phil," said Ivan.

I risked looking away from the pick of my axe to see where we were headed. The rope continued another twenty yards before ending at an ice screw. I hoped to see a ledge or something. There was no ledge. The angle of the slope eased off a bit but it still looked really steep.

A loud voice behind me.

I looked back at Ang. Our eyes connected. He looked like he was staring across the river Styx. The sherpa wasn't the one making noise, though.

The lead Italian climber, dressed in bright red and lime green, was speaking English. I couldn't make out the words. He saw me watching and yelled.

"Hurry fuck up!"

That sonuvabitch. Fuck you. I mouthed the two words.

His face contorted beneath his sunglasses.

"This our mountain, you motherfucker!" he shouted back.

The climber behind him leaned out to have a look. It wasn't one of the Italians. It was Varney.

"I'll unclip him," said the ghoul in a calm, quiet church voice I could somehow hear. "Unclip him and then just a little push."

Varney's pale, ungloved hand actually reached out. It came to rest almost tenderly on the furious man's shoulder. I was angry; pissed off that the climber was chirping, and pissed off that his meaningless belligerence had conjured my nasty hallucination. In that moment, I *wanted* to see the red and green-clad figure shake loose and float down into oblivion. I wanted to see the Italian's sneering face shocked into an expression of complete surprise. I'd wave like the Queen. Smile like her, too.

"No."

I said the word aloud. If Ang heard me talking to myself he gave no indication. Varney heard, though. His hand paused then changed direction slightly, no longer a push but a pinch with thumb and index finger. His claws closed over the arm of the Italian's sunglasses right at the temple. Then he pulled the glasses off the man's face.

The mirrored lenses flashed twice as they tumbled and vanished into the void.

The climber didn't fall but I did get to see that expression: the look of complete, stunned surprise. My reaction was borne of complete shock. I burst into laughter. Varney beamed back, his freaky round mouth forming an upturned crescent.

The climber thought it was joy on my face – maybe it was – and he screamed something in Italian. He lunged forward, crowding up against Ang.

The sherpa's response was instant. His face transformed into a gargoyle snarl. Before Ang could turn to the Italian and say something, though, the encroaching climber reached up and unclipped himself. The Italian threw his arm over my teammate's shoulders to plant the tip of his axe into the ice face beyond Ang.

The man was in a boiling fit of rage and he was coming for me. His swing succeeded in burying the pick into the mountain. It also succeeded in clotheslining Ang in the back of the head, smashing the sherpa face-first into blue ice. Before my colleague had even begun to recover, the European launched himself across Ang's back, reaching with his left foot to clear the sherpa's legs.

It was incredibly reckless: If the tool wasn't secure, he'd fall. The tool wasn't the problem, though. The problem was my make-believe monster.

As the Italian lunged with his left foot, he tried to push off with his right. Varney jammed his own foot into the back of the aggressor's right foot, holding it in place. Instead of clearing Ang, the jumper was locked diagonally across the sherpa's back, his fully-extended left arm attached to the handle of an ice axe and his twisted right foot stuck back where he began.

A great roar spat out of Ang's bleeding mouth. He threw his head back. His helmet smashed into the Italian's nose. The pick of my would-be assailant's axe popped loose. He started to fall.

Varney kept the climber's foot jammed in place. The Italian swung upside down, his trapped boot acting as a fulcrum. There was a loud 'pop' as the weight of his body exceeded his tibia's ability to bend. The man screamed.

I screamed, too, a strangled choke of shock. Ang stared at the wall in front of him, blinking snow out of his face. And Varney still had the man's boot locked into the ice. My delusion, my fantasy, was the only thing keeping the victim attached to the mountain.

Varney would let him drop. I knew he would. The creature's dead-insect face looked even more jovial than before.

Ang looked to his right and immediately understood the Italian's predicament. The sherpa reached out with his own foot to trap the man's boot in the ice. Varney moved his foot the moment before the sherpa touched it. The stricken man screamed but stayed securely in place.

Ivan was past me before it even registered the guide was in motion. The Ukrainian down-climbed the ice in seconds, bringing himself even with the injured party, albeit upright rather than inverted.

"Chrissakes, what happened?" Ivan yelled. It was the first time I'd heard him even a little unhinged.

Finally words issued from my mouth instead of peals of laughter.

"He tried – he tried to pass Ang – he fell."

That was what happened, wasn't it? What would be the point of mentioning Varney's role in the tragedy? Varney wasn't real.

The phantom looked real, though, sitting cross-legged on an outcrop of rock five feet from Ivan. The Ukrainian used one hand to attach himself to the wall with his axe while the other was pulling a length of cord from his harness. Varney craned his neck around Ivan to get a good view of the rescue. His neck stretched too far, like those women in Myanmar with rings stacked around their necks.

Ang stared straight ahead, the blood around his mouth already frozen.

"Get Phil moving," Ivan called up to the sherpa. Then he told me not to move, "not until Ang reaches you."

The next Italian climber in line reached his fallen comrade. The last member of their rope moved up another few metres. The one beside Ivan said something harsh-sounding in our direction. This time I didn't mouth any words back.

Ang was facing me, his feet slowly kicking a route along the tracks left by our guide. The whole scene looked fake, like the people were little clay figures. Tendrils of blackness streaked the edge of my vision and my heart raced. I tried to slow my breathing, tried to expand my chest with each intake. My left ankle was aching and my right calf felt like a stab of agony. My shoulders burned as I grasped the ice axe with both hands.

Ang passed behind me. I said sorry into the snow. I don't know if he heard. Then he was on the other side of me, in the lead.

"Come on," he said.

The sherpa started walking along the tight rope of snow at the foot of the glacier. I edged along sideways like before. I glanced back at Ivan. The fallen climber was wailing, a keening agony that echoed off the ice. His broken leg was terrible, twisted a complete one-eighty, only wrecked muscle and a down suit keeping him attached to his wedged foot.

An injury like that was nasty on a football field. At twenty-seven thousand feet, it was likely fatal.

I looked over at Ang. He faced up the path away from me. We were getting close. A few more steps and we'd be starting the final snowfields.

My arms started to shake. I was gripping too hard. I'd lost feeling in all the toes of my left foot. They didn't hurt. You'd think frostbite would. Maybe the tumour was helping me out, blocking pain receptors in my brain. Maybe I didn't have frostbite at all. Perhaps the final stage of my cancer was a creeping paralysis, beginning at the feet. Staying on the summit waiting for death would certainly be an easy choice if I couldn't move.

"Okay," said Ang. "We wait."

We were at the end of the fixed rope but remained clipped to it. I lowered the axe and used the adze on the back to chip a platform out of the crusted snow. I parked my right boot in it. Then I worked at widening the platform until it would accommodate my other foot as well. At first I faced out but that was way too scary. I turned sideways and looked back towards Ivan. That was pretty terrifying, too, but I focused on the figures struggling to help the fallen climber.

The last member of the first Italian team had joined his injured teammate, his arrival delayed – as all things were at this altitude – by exhaustion and caution. Ivan was talking to them. One of them was making gestures with his right hand. He pointed in our direction. All three men looked at us, then turned back to the injured climber.

"What do you think they're talking about?" I asked Ang.

116

He didn't answer so I repeated the question.

"How to get him down the mountain," the sherpa answered.

I didn't feel bad. No remorse or empathy had been triggered. Weird, I suppose. I was aware of the importance of him living, certainly, I just had no emotional attachment to it happening.

I wondered if Ang felt the same way.

I wondered which of us bore more responsibility for what happened. Probably me. There was no sense of guilt attached to that assessment. What would be the point? The climber was way over there, a casualty on his way down the hill, while I was still bound for the top. Different worlds. He was a starving man in Zambia while I was tucking into a tall stack of pancakes at the IHOP. His need – his hunger – had no impact on my appetite.

Ivan climbed back up to the fixed line. The injured Italian was finally upright, held to the wall with ice screws and attended by his two teammates. The second Italian rope team had reached the point on the traverse where the accident occurred.

It only took Ivan a moment to join us.

"What the hell?" said the guide. He was looking at me. I shrugged.

I turned and looked at Ang. He was staring upslope, eyes fixed on the summit snowfields. Varney was standing behind him. The beast's arms passed under the sherpa's armpits, and its two claws gripped Ang's chest like they were cupping breasts. Foam and ichor slid down its formless chin. A thin tube of tongue extended out of the gaping circular mouth and wended its way through the bristle of transparent fangs.

Ang stared uphill and Varney stared at me. The creature leaned forward until it looked like its glassy teeth were scraping against the sirdar's right ear.

"Whatever," Ivan continued. "It's just after eleven. We're still at least three hours from the summit. And that's if you don't slow down more. I think we need to turn around. They need all the hands they can get. They think it's our fault, so it might spare us some grief if we pitch in."

"Not our fault," said Ang. Varney's mouth was moving, like he was whispering into the sherpa's ear.

"No one made him unclip," I added. I hung on to that truth as Ivan frowned and searched my face.

"You don't want to help?" said the Ukrainian.

I looked back at Ang. His gaze was still firmly fixed on the snowfields above us. Varney's eyes had grown, the perfect fisheye circle of each flattening where

117

they met in the middle of his face. I looked at Ivan, felt the pressure of his expectations.

"I do," I said. "I want to help. But we're so close. We can help when we get back."

Ivan shook his head.

"The longer it takes getting him down," he said, "the greater the chance he doesn't make it. Isn't the opportunity to be a hero worth losing the summit?"

Ang's voice was loud: "He won't make it. People die. If it's his time..."

"That's Buddhist bullshit, Ang."

It was the first time I'd heard anger in Ivan's voice when he was addressing the sherpa. "He made a mistake," Ivan continued, "but we're tied up in this."

"We'll sort out," said Ang. "But first climb."

I couldn't tell if the conversation was as weird as it seemed to me or if my brain was finally calling it quits. Suddenly I felt like I was no longer the reason we were on the mountain, like there was a contest of wills between these two best friends. That made no sense at all.

"I say we go down and it's my call to make," said Ivan.

I looked past him to the Italian team. They'd hoisted the injured man up to the traverse. A hundred feet away from me. A million miles. I wanted nothing to do with recriminations or even redemption. Not anymore. I was in the death zone.

"I have to keep going."

I said it in a low voice but Ivan heard me.

"You're coming back down with me," he countered.

I shook my head. I gave him a sad frown.

"I can't. Not going that direction. I have to climb," I said.

I didn't say he had to come with me – but I didn't say he didn't have to, either.

Ivan had a million-dollar deposit, the rest to be paid when my suicide trip was finished. If I died on K2, barring obvious evidence of foul play, he'd get the full amount. Our agreement was simple: he had to get me as high as he could without risking his own life "beyond the standard to which he usually climbed."

Ivan's standard, however, included feats like free-soloing K2's notorious serac. There was no clause exempting him from his obligations in order to rescue someone. Would I screw Ivan out of his compensation if he chose to lead a man back to life instead of taking me to my death? No. I wasn't that heartless. I was, however, heartless enough to leave the question in Ivan's mind.

The guide bit his lip. He was about to speak when Ang interrupted him.

"I am going up, Ivan. You come too. You come to summit and I help with Italy when return Camp Four. If he can be saved, you and I will do it."

The Ukrainian's mouth thinned and the muscles bulged in his jaw.

"And if I don't?" said Ivan.

What the sherpa said next was, I'm sure, inexplicable to Ivan. Ang was being paid out of the expedition budget. He'd get a summit bonus if we topped out, but it was only twenty percent. What Ivan couldn't see was the oozing mouth hole of my imaginary Varney scratching at his climbing partner's ear. Ang's next words were a napalm strike on a friendly village, an arclight demolition of trust and brotherhood.

"Then when come back, I not help. In Base Camp I tell everyone I was on summit with Phil, not you. I say you abandon client."

I didn't know if it was Varney's voice I heard in my head or my own.

You're a piece of shit.

119

PART III

CHAPTER TWENTY-TWO

JULY 30

IVAN AND ANG hadn't spoken in more than an hour. An hour? I didn't know. Time had stopped. The plod up the summit cone was endless. At least Varney hadn't reappeared.

The numbness in my toes had spread up my left foot to the ankle. Wouldn't that be a conversation piece if I returned to Halifax to die: "Yes, I lost the foot on K2 a couple of weeks ago."

Sounded like bragging. I'd said good-bye to my life. Better to end it here.

We were behind schedule. I knew that much. It had to be early afternoon. My watch was buried beneath three layers. I should have had it strapped outside my down suit. I'd thought the final part of the climb would be less steep than it was. I paused after every step and wheezed until my harness was yanked. Ivan was short-roping me and I was water-skiing behind him; he was trying not to pull me up the mountain and I was trying my best not to be pulled. Neither of us was having great success.

That first section after the traverse was hairy. Ivan and Ang were barking at each other. They argued: short, nasty statements; a harsh exchange they'd always remember, even if the friendship survived. No one was talking to me. I was just trying not to slide off the mountain. The snow was deep and light. It felt like there was nothing to grab onto. It slipped and vanished when you tried to bury your axe, and the slope at that point was more than sixty-degrees. I was constantly on the verge of sliding.

Then the angle eased and the snow condensed. The wind picked up. I was colder but falling became less of a concern.

The cold was otherworldly. I knew it would be nasty. It had to be minus thirty at least. Add in a brisk breeze and the conditions were Antarctic. The objective temperature only told part of the story, though. Altitude and dehydration made circulation slow down and put digits at risk. My hands felt stiff. It could just be the death grip I'd had on my axe through the technical sections of the climb earlier, but it could also be frostbite.

I looked over at Ang. He was five metres away, walking beside me. With us, but apart. He was the one who insisted on helping me to the top yet he felt more distant than Ivan.

Ivan had to be angry with me. We could have been saving a life. We could have been almost back to Camp Four. Instead we were on my mission. Something in me should have felt bad about that, I supposed. Every minute we spent moving up was a minute we could have been moving down, moving closer to saving the fallen Italian.

But we were so close to finishing.

I didn't feel guilty. I felt fear and fatigue, an emptiness so complete it registered as pain, and a nearly overwhelming urge to stop moving. My heart hammered. My lungs rasped. Thank god my left foot was numb because my right foot screamed like an open wound. Even that pain was surpassed, however, by the deep wrongness aching in my thighs and lower back. Every step they spoke to me. No. No. No.

I had a headache, of course. Pretty much everyone has a headache in the death zone, but I knew it was more than that. Cancer filled my skull. My face, my neck, my back pulsed with it.

There was anger there, too. Simmering rage pushed against the headache, pushed against my weakness. Hatred lashed out at my cancer, and at the man injured in the traverse as well. I was angry that he'd forced me to choose, that his stupidity weighed me down when I was already carrying so much to the top of the goddamn hill.

I owed him nothing. I owed nothing to anyone. Whatever remorse I felt about coercing Ivan was useless. A human emotion in the wrong time and place. The world had become elemental. Ice and pain and burning.

"Move faster," said Ivan.

I was standing still. He was tugging on the rope. I wasn't sure when I'd taken my last step.

"I'm not dying up here, Phil, so find another gear or I'm leaving," he said.

Ang didn't join the exchange. He took two steps and paused for a few lungfuls of air.

"Okay," I gasped.

It took me fifteen seconds to recover from speaking, but then I lifted my right foot and planted it in the print left by my guide. Ivan turned and continued plodding upwards. I could see the sky above us, where the mountain reached clear blue and then stopped. It looked like the summit was right there. That was an illusion. I knew we hadn't been walking long enough to be at the top.

I looked back the way we'd come. The slope fell steeply, a broad white hill ending in air. Our footprints were still visible although the wind was blowing snow across them.

The rope pulled and I stepped. The rope pulled and I stepped.

Did I have any water left? I didn't remember the last time I'd drunk water. Were we in the Bottleneck? Water in the Bottleneck? That struck me as funny. I smiled. I didn't feel like myself. I felt stupid, all fuzzy around the edges.

The black that ringed my eyesight lower down had encroached further into my field of vision. The air had two-thirds less oxygen by volume than it had at sea level. My muscles were starving. My brain cells were starving. My body was dying. It was already dying from cancer, but this was more acute. Getting to the summit of an eight-thousander is a mad dash into an environment that won't sustain life.

I wondered how quickly we could get back down. It had to be after two o'clock. What time did the 2008 climbers reach the top? A bunch of them ended up having to bivouac before descending. Even the ones who headed directly down went through the traverse and Bottleneck in the dark. Both scenarios were scary.

"We'll take a break," said Ivan.

He didn't sit down. None of us did. Sit down and you might not have the energy to get back up. I swayed in the wind. Whatever water I had left was unreachable in my backpack; exerting the effort to get it was inconceivable. Thirst was easier.

A break from the climb was welcome, however. I wanted to ask how much further we had to go but the words stuck in my throat. I would walk until I reached the top or I couldn't walk. It would take *some* amount of time, it didn't matter how long. Knowing wouldn't make it any easier.

"We caught a nice day," said Ivan. "Last time I was up here we had gusts over sixty. Makes a big difference. The cold, the effort. This is good. Our weather streak continues."

I managed a nod to indicate I'd heard.

"Gotta be quick going down, though," he said. "Storm's not supposed to move in until late tomorrow night, but those clouds don't look good."

I made the effort to turn my head. I saw clouds beyond Chogolisa, a peak overlooking Concordia. Hard to tell how close they were. Didn't look ominous to me but what did I know about clouds?

"I want to keep going," I said, the most words I'd spoken since the traverse.

"Yeah, I got that," he said. He spoke again, over his shoulder, before he started walking: "You'll be gone soon, Phil. Now's the time to use whatever you've got left. I won't carry you."

The first two steps, one with the right, one with the left. They felt impossible, like there was no way my legs would actually respond to the instructions I was sending them. But they did answer the call, at least a little. Then the next pair of steps was slightly steadier.

Ivan was right. He was speaking out of anger but he was right. No point saving anything for later. If I reached the summit a dried, empty husk, the wind could carry me away.

Come on, you soft bastard, what are you made of?

I was doing it. My feet rose and swung forward. I don't know how. Nothing about the way I felt indicated I should be capable of movement. Ivan was no longer pulling on the rope. I kept it slack between us.

Ang was keeping pace, of course. He actually smoked a cigarette after the fight with Ivan. I wondered how easy this really was for him. Maybe he just cultivated the appearance of ease. The sherpas never looked exhausted.

It was strange to think of people who weren't there with us. The sherpas in Camp Two boiling snow for water. The Italians in their Camp Four tents. Raymond at Base Camp.

Karen in Nova Scotia.

Karen was real. Many thousands of miles away, there was a place I had called home. It was home with her. And I lost it. Now another man had my place. They would continue for many years, decades after this day.

Ivan had a satellite phone. When I got to the top, I'd ask to use it. It was for emergencies and this was an emergency. I needed to speak to Karen one more time. Maybe not even that. Maybe I just needed to hear her voice.

I'd get to do that when I reached the top.

CHAPTER TWENTY-THREE

JULY 30

HAPPINESS FOUND ME.

I don't know how. Everything hurt. My nose was definitely frozen. I had only the vaguest sensation in my left leg below the knee, and the toes of my right foot were burning with cold. Joy filled my heaving chest, however, and swelled my straining heart.

We weren't even to the top yet. I could see it, though. Ivan said it really was the end. A hundred metres and I could stop. It seemed impossible I'd be able to cover that distance but I knew I would.

I was going to make it.

"It's incredible," I whispered.

I was surprised: I'd worried I wouldn't feel anything. All the effort, all the time, a dying man's final wish, and all along I suspected I would reach the top and feel nothing. Numb. A nihilist's negation of all human ambition. It turns out, I cared very much. It mattered to me.

I looked back at Ang. He'd moved, tucking in behind me.

"Almost there," I croaked at him.

I couldn't see his face or hear his response. The wind had picked up. Goggles saved my eyes from snow blindness but they couldn't clear the gale from the sky, or the driving snow that came with it.

The rope tugged on my harness. Ivan was unstoppable. He was going to succeed. He was going to get me to the top. I took two steps closer. My lungs bellowed and I coughed from the dry, cold air.

The turmoil in my body wasn't matched by my mind. All the strain, all the effort, all the damage, and I felt peace.

Imagine that. Wanting nothing. Expecting nothing.

I was splitting in two. I could feel my body flailing, failing, pushed far beyond a limit that seemed inconceivable just weeks before. But I also felt light, each step lighter, like I might start lifting off the mountain. Something had broken loose in my chest and my skull: a titanium-foil balloon filled with I-dunno-what – consciousness, star stuff, *soul* – bounced around and batted off clumsy walls of bone and meat. Waiting to be set free.

Wanting to soar.

I smiled. My cheeks were cracking cardboard. Didn't matter. Ivan turned to me. "It's right there," he said. "C'mon."

Fifty metres. I counted to twenty and moved a single boot. Ivan was waiting. Ang was behind me but I didn't have the energy to look.

I was supposed to phone Karen. That had been important to me. I didn't care. It was a thousand lifetimes ago. I would be alone soon. Uncontained. The rest wouldn't matter ever again.

Ivan pulled on the rope, reminding me to move. I wasn't there yet. Did I even need to keep going, complete the formality of touching that particular point in space? I suppose I still did. The movement felt like a kind of progress, a painful process required to finally break the prison that held me in.

I had a strong urge to piss so I soaked the inner layer of my thermals. It didn't matter. The warmth felt good. It might not feel good later but later didn't exist.

"You're so close, Phil. It's almost time."

The words brushed my ear. I looked for the speaker. I expected Varney to be sitting in miniature on my shoulder, whispering in his inhuman voice. I didn't see him.

The angle of the slope eased. My eyes were coming level with, yes, with the top! How could that be possible? I could see the actual highest point of the mountain. Ivan had stopped moving. He turned. He smiled the drunk smile from the first night at Base Camp, only now the drug was oxygen deprivation.

Three more steps. Would something stop me? I raised my foot.

Two. Suddenly it seemed too easy, like succeeding shouldn't have been possible. Where are you Varney? I want to laugh in your horrendous face.

One...

...then I was facing Ivan, standing where he stood. He took a step over and put his arm across my shoulders. I looked over the far side of the mountain, into China.

"You made it, buddy. You made it."

Ivan was choking up. His eyes were filled with warmth. The power of the peak: all was forgiven. I turned, looking for the third member of our party.

Ang was standing in our final bootprints, not at the top with us, still ten feet from the summit. Ivan beckoned him over. Ang smiled.

"I'm sorry," said the sherpa when he reached us. Ivan pulled him into an embrace with his right arm and scooped me in with his left. High altitude is a mind bender. It could trigger a scorching disagreement or the most unlikely generosity.

It could also knock you off your feet. I lost my balance and fell on my ass. Ivan was reaching out for me even as I dropped. He stopped when he realized I was still smiling.

"You okay?" he said.

I nodded, too out of breath to speak. The black rings around my vision had closed in more; my view was reduced by half. Tendrils of starry dark streamed across my pupils.

"You take picture," Ang said to Ivan, handing my camera to our leader. The sherpa had carried it for me. They carried everything for me. I never would have made it without Ang and Ivan.

"Okay," said Ivan, "you stand beside Phil. Squat down Ang, squat down beside him."

Ang was still on his feet but down in a crouch beside me, one hand balanced on my shoulder, the other clutching his ice axe. Ivan had the camera raised to his face. He was peering through the aperture.

"Okay, ready," said Ivan.

"No, I won't," said Ang softly.

"What?" I said to the sherpa.

"I can't," he whispered.

Ivan was still behind the camera: "Say 'Cheese!'"

I wasn't smiling at the camera. I was staring at Ang.

My stomach plummeted. Something was terribly wrong. Was I finally having that heart attack?

Before I could utter a sound, the sherpa was on his feet and sprinting towards our leader. It only took a second for him to cover the fifteen or so feet. Ang's right arm was a blur of motion. The ice axe flashed silver as it arced towards its target.

The sound of impact. I could hear it clearly over the growl of the wind. A tenderizing hammer striking a thick slab of flank steak.

Chunk.

Ivan fell to the ground. The axe swung again.

Chunk.

CHAPTER TWENTY-FOUR

JULY 30

ANG STOOD STILL. Ivan was motionless at the sherpa's feet. I was motionless because I was still too exhausted to move.

The ice axe was embedded in Ivan's chest. Ang was panting. Sprinting and killing were difficult with two-thirds less oxygen.

The sherpa was talking to Ivan. He was whispering. Then the volume increased. There was a note of panic in the voice, a sound utterly foreign to the calm and determined timbre of Ang's usual tone.

"...say he save my son, Ivan. He save Nima! And still I am no, I not do it..."

Ivan blinked. "I don't understand," he said.

"He take my hands, Ivan. He make me! You have to help. You are my only friend. You have to help me..."

Ang's voice trailed off. A shudder passed through his body and he stood more erect. He looked up at me and his legs started moving. A huge surge of adrenaline brought me from a seated position to my knees but I hadn't even started to stand when the sherpa reached me. He placed a hand on my climbing helmet and, with a single easy push, knocked me back down. I stared into his panicked eyes. His mouth twisted in agony.

"No. No!" he gasped.

His hand grabbed the handle of the small climbing knife he kept lashed to the shoulder strap of his summit pack. The blade was soundless as he pulled it free of its sheath.

"What if this is it, Phil? What if this is your end?"

Ang was gone. It was Varney speaking. Varney holding the dagger.

"What if I slice open your belly, stuff my face into your gaping guts, and eat my way through to your spine?" it said.

Such joy in that voice. I couldn't speak. I was hyperventilating. Swallowing mouthfuls of useless, denuded air. You're not real, this isn't real, I've gone crazy, I'm asleep in my tent, I'm asleep in bed, I never left Karen, this is all a terrible dream.

I closed my eyes and opened them again, hoping to reboot reality – and it worked. It was Ang holding the dagger again, Ang reaching out to me with a shaking hand.

"Please, no!" I shouted.

A flash of silver. I turned my head and raised my hands. But the blow never fell.

I looked up. The knife was buried in Ang's neck.

A hoarse cry escaped my raw throat. Blood drenched his hand. His mouth worked, tried to voice words. Then the lips curled up into a grimace. He stared into my eyes. Anguish radiated from his gaze but there was something else there, too. Triumph, perhaps, or maybe just anger. The grim pleasure of a final, stubborn victory.

The sirdar turned. He staggered one step towards Ivan and let go of the knife hilt. A fresh jet of crimson fountained across the snow. The sherpa reached towards his best friend with a dripping, scarlet hand.

The drops froze before they touched the ground. A blast of cold air hit him with the force of a locomotive. The sheen of fresh blood on Ang's shoulders dulled instantly. He was two metres from me – fighting in death to reach the friend he'd murdered – and then he was a hundred metres away and fifty feet above me, sailing through the orange sky. It looked ridiculous, like a figure from a cartoon, or a caped hero in a movie.

The sherpa was a colourful dot half a kilometre into China before he began to arc downwards out of my sight.

CHAPTER TWENTY-FIVE

JULY 30

I DON'T KNOW how long I sat at the summit before I finally heard the voice.

"Phil."

So faint. The sound of a ghost.

I allowed gravity to pull me sideways. I turned face down just before I made contact with the snow. I breathed, then, inflating my lungs four times before expending the effort to rise onto my hands and knees. I crawled through red hoar frost – Ang must have been real, here was proof – and reached Ivan. I dropped my face onto the ice beside his cheek.

"Did you see that?" he whispered.

I didn't know. I had a memory that couldn't be real.

"Did *you* see it?" I asked. Wetness from my nose slipped on his ear.

"Ang. He was flying. It was amazing," said Ivan.

Yes he was. The wind took him. It didn't touch me. It didn't touch Ivan. It picked the sherpa like an assassin's bullet.

"I think something's wrong with me," I said. "I think I'm dying. I'm seeing things."

A rasping cough. An attempt at laughter.

"We're all dying. We all see things," said Ivan.

We fell silent then. Neither of us spoke until the guide surprised me with a wet, cracking cough.

"Go down," he said.

I was cold. It was the first time I'd noticed since Ang attacked. My feet felt like wood and the fingers of my left hand ached.

The guide gasped, followed by a terrible sound of choking. Air gurgled out of two holes in his chest.

"Get up Phil. You have to go."

Ivan couldn't climb back down and neither could I. I won't pretend it was only because I wouldn't abandon him. I was fixed with fear. The thought of trying to descend alone was scarier than the prospect of death; slipping into hypothermia was far preferable to slipping into a chasm, being avalanched off the mountain or crushed by a serac.

Far better than being alone in the dark waiting for the return of Varney.

"Right behind you, Phil."

"Just catching my breath," I said. "Need rest. Then we go."

Ivan actually moved. He grabbed the back of my jacket and pulled on the garment. There was still strength in his grip.

"Can't stay here," he said.

"We won't."

He let go, then used the gloved hand to slap the back of my helmet.

"Must get lower."

"We will," I said.

I wanted him to stop fighting. *I* wanted to stop fighting. I'd been fighting forever. I was ready to rest. It wasn't acceptance of death, so much as hatred of effort. So tired. I felt utterly depleted. Just the idea of movement made me tear up.

Ivan tried to raise his torso. I felt him wince.

I forced myself to sit up. I'd avoided touching the embedded ice axe. I recalled first aid advice about not removing large objects when they've pierced the body. An axe is a large object. It could be plugging the wound. If I took it out, Ivan might drain onto the slope in minutes.

The guide started to roll onto his side. He pulled his knees up and reached across his chest with a hand. He was trying to get into a crawling position.

"No," I said.

That didn't stop him. I don't know where he found the strength.

He kept turning until he succeeded. His body hunched over the embedded axe and his forehead touched the frozen ground. I leaned down until my face was right up against his.

"You need to rest," I said.

"Fuck that. Get lower."

Was he going to start crawling down the mountain? That couldn't be possible, even for Ivan. Joe Simpson touched the void and crawled out of it. Beck Weathers all but froze to death on Everest, thawed, and then lurched down the mountain, albeit with lots of help. But surely Ivan's condition was magnitudes worse? His wounds would be fatal even at sea level.

"My pack. Red bag," he gasped.

I opened the top of his summit bag, still strapped on his back. I pulled out a small, red nylon bag. I unzipped the cover, revealing its spare contents. First aid this high up came down to essentials: drugs. I thought Ang carried the meds, but here was a chemical heating pouch and four identical, unfrozen syringes. I took out one, almost fumbling it in the snow with my frozen, gloved fingers.

"In the thigh," Ivan mumbled.

I used my teeth to pull the plastic cover off the needle. I pushed the sharp point into the thigh of his down suit and depressed the plunger. I started to count. At four Ivan took a deep breath. I could see his body shudder with the effort.

"Christ," he muttered. Not loud but no longer a whisper either. The guide pushed himself into a table stance and then leaned back. His hands left the ground. He knelt on his haunches, the plastic syringe still sticking out of his leg.

Ivan turned his head slowly. His eyes were clear – that was good – but his face was taut and stretched.

"Now you," he said.

I took a second syringe out of the pack and plunged the needle into my left thigh. I couldn't feel its bite, not even when I depressed the plunger.

One, two…

Oh wow. Okay, wow.

Energy radiated out of my heart, pulsed toward my extremities. It was like a nuclear reactor had lit up my chest. I was Ironman.

"That's the good stuff," I gulped.

Ivan blinked. His pupils were huge.

"Dex. It won't last," he said.

I thought the dexamethasone – used to treat cerebral and pulmonary edema in the mountains – was in Ang's pack.

"For altitude sickness?" I said.

Ivan shook his head. "Amphetamine," he said.

Speed. Used by German soldiers as they swept across Europe, and by football players in subsequent decades as they blitzed their opponents on the gridiron. Not a standard fixture on climbing expeditions. A desperation drug for a heroic final effort.

He shrugged off his summit bag. I couldn't imagine how much pain he was feeling every time he moved. In the top pouch he'd stashed a spare pair of wool gloves and a small spool of duct tape.

"Need to pull out this axe," he said.

"That's a bad idea," I said. As I rose to my feet stars shimmered across my narrowed vision. It had to be getting late in the day yet the ambient light had become as bright as noon.

"No. Can't move with this. Come on. Help."

I stood in front of the guide. He told me to wrap my hand around the head of the axe at the point where it pierced his chest.

"On three, pull...," he said. I waited for further instruction. Finally he could speak again.

"...I pass out, pack holes with mitts."

"And use the tape?"

He nodded.

Maybe this could work. He was Ivan the fuckin' Terrible, dammit. He'd live because he wouldn't give his body another option.

"Three, two...one," I counted.

I pulled the axe with all my altitude-weakened strength, trying to keep a slight arc to the movement. I was worried the teeth on the pick would get stuck on a rib.

Ivan screamed. It was a horrible sound, too high, like a lamb being devoured by a jackal. The axe wasn't coming out smoothly. I had two inches of red-coated metal but there had to be another three inches to come. Ivan toppled sideways as I tried to apply more pressure. The pick threatened to twist free of my grip but then I felt it snap past a bone and come loose.

I dropped the axe in the snow. It started to slide. The slope was gentle at the summit but metal offers no friction. I managed to grab the tool before it was out of reach. I swung the axe to bury the pick in the ground. The sound on impact reminded me of Ang's work.

"Wake up, Ivan."

He didn't respond. His eyes were closed. I pulled off my left mitt. My pinkie finger and ring finger were white. There was a dark brown tinge to the tip of the pinkie. I clumsily tried to pull down the zipper of the guide's down suit. It wouldn't budge. He'd have two more layers underneath. Even if I got down to bare skin, he'd need to be covered immediately or he'd die of exposure.

"I'm still here," Ivan coughed.

I felt a spark of joy despite the circumstances. I told the guide I couldn't undo the zipper. He said to stuff the mitts into the holes in the suit. There was no blood pouring from the gash in the fabric but when I pushed the mitt in, I could immediately feel wet warmth. His chest under the outer layer was soaked. I tried to wiggle my two limber fingers into the tear, probing for the actual wound. Then my fingers sank deep. I could feel the fibrillations of his racing heart.

"Christ!" I instinctively pulled my hand out. It was stained red-black. "Oh Jesus, Jesus."

I pushed the fingers back in and shoved the mitt into the yawning gash, careful not to push too hard at the deepest point.

"Tape, Phil. Can you get tape in?"

135

Ivan's voice was growing faint again. I thought about the remaining syringe. His heart rate had to be close to 200 beats per minute. Any stimulant now might kill him.

I tried for five minutes to get a piece of tape through the gore-soaked tear, into the suit and secured to his slippery skin. It was useless.

"Let me get the other hole," I said.

The second one was deep as well. There was less blood but I could feel air vibrating in and out of it each time he took a rasping breath. I stuffed a mitt into that hole, too.

"I need to sit you up," I said.

I got behind the guide and propped him into a seated position. Then I wrapped tape all the way around his chest, passing it under his arms and over the mitten-stuffed holes. I did two circuits before silver star trails started crossing my vision. I took that as a warning to stop moving for a moment. I sat down from my half-kneeling position.

"We sit here, we die," he wheezed.

Ivan was still conscious.

"What time is it?" I asked.

"Dunno. Must be four. Need to get lower before we bivvy."

Bivouac overnight, outside, above 8,000 metres. We'd sleep tucked in the arms of death. Very few wake from that slumber.

I nodded. I nodded again, this time to myself. Come on, Phil. You're not a quitter. You didn't come to K2 to quit. You came to live like you've never lived before.

Ivan is alive and you need to save him.

I planted both hands on the icy surface beside me. I rose to a kneel and then lifted a crampon until it bit into the snow. Could I actually stand up? I could. I still wasn't sure I wanted to walk – surrendering would have been so much easier – but getting to my feet took a lot of effort; it would be a shame not to take advantage of it.

I kicked out a foot. The weight of my boot propelled me forward a step. There was a satisfying crunch as the teeth of the crampons pierced the ground. Thank god the snow wasn't deep. It would be deep lower down the mountain but that was a lifetime away. I'd worry about that when the impossible happened and I made it off the summit. I lowered my right hand and took a weak swipe at Ivan's shoulder.

"Here," I offered.

He took the grip. I almost tumbled on top of him when he pulled. I was surprised by the strength in his arms.

He was on his feet. We were both standing.

"You got everything?" Ivan asked.

I didn't answer. I had no idea. What did I need? We were walking before I even fully thought about the simple question.

Did I have everything? Sure. I had my summit. At a heavy cost, though. One of us was dead, another was the walking dead and the third was the soon-to-be dead. Ivan and I could trade those last two titles back and forth.

We weren't roped together. No point when neither of us had the strength to save the other. Ivan was behind me. Our tracks from the ascent were still faintly visible. The sun looked low. It had to be closer to five, if not later. I hoped the sunlight remained until we reached the traverse. Fixed ropes would show us the route once we were there. Up on the summit snowfields, though, it would be easy to end up at the wrong place – perched at the top of a sheer drop with no route down.

I felt terrible. Ivan was beyond running on fumes. We'd need at least three hours to the traverse. I tried to remember if the moon was almost full. Clouds scudded above us. Wouldn't it be lovely if we were in a full blizzard when night fell.

I stopped to rest. I looked back towards the top. That was the summit. I stood there. Despite what happened – and despite the misery I knew lay ahead – it still had the power to amaze me. I'd walked where only gods were meant to be.

"Move," Ivan wheezed.

The adrenaline was fading. I felt like the mountain was absorbing my energy with each step, recharging its malevolence, building the power to lash out at us. The wind kept building, too. It had to be over eighty kilometres. It was at our backs but I still had to be careful. The slope was steep, almost cleared of snow. Blue ice cracked beneath my crampons. One misstep and I'd rocket downhill and into space.

The tracks grew faint as the remaining snow scudded away. I fixed my eyes on a distant peak beyond the pattern of boot prints: that was the direction down to the traverse. It was a narrow passage – too far right and we'd be on top of sheer cliffs – too far left and we'd end up at the edge of the glacier overhanging the Bottleneck.

The sun was just above the jagged horizon. K2 cast a shadow across the world.

I'd forgotten to call Karen. It had been so important to me on the way up. I'd have to wait until we got back to camp. I couldn't imagine trying to get the sat phone out of Ivan's pack. My left hand tingled. Pulses of pain radiated from the palm out to the frozen fingertips. My right hand was still okay. I needed my hands, one hand at least, or I'd be done.

"We made it."

Ivan's voice was a croak. I didn't know what he was talking about.

137

"What?"

He was wheezing.

"Top of K2. You did it."

Happiness in the midst of the mental horror and physical agony. I felt it wash over me, filling in the gaps where the drugs were fading.

I was always going to die. Ivan and Ang were always going to die. Our stories always end the same way, every one of us. But goddamn if I didn't make it a helluva final chapter. My feet felt light again and I stood straighter.

Ivan was talking to himself. I couldn't make out the words. I heard the name Ang a couple of times. I didn't stop.

The sun dipped below the mountains. I could still make out the peak that guided us but our footprints were gone. Time was running out. The slope never ended. Deeper snow had reappeared, slowed our effort. I tried to calculate how quickly we were moving but it was useless. My dying brain didn't want to work. Even going downhill I had to gasp three times between each step. The wind had gained even more strength. White swirled around me, threatened my equilibrium. It looked like the end of the world. We were astronauts shipwrecked on a lethal planet and Earth was fifty light-years away.

I heard a statue crumple behind me. I took another two breaths before mustering the energy to turn and look back. Ivan was lying in the snow. He was ten feet back. Uphill. An impossible distance.

I stumbled to his side. I was, apparently, still capable of impossible things.

"Get up," I said to him. My voice was calm.

"Yes," he said. He didn't move.

"Get up."

I reached down and grabbed his outstretched hand. I leaned back, tried to use my weight to lift him. He managed to sit up but that's as far as he got. The front of his down suit was black with frozen blood.

"Go," he said.

"Not without you."

He shook his head.

"It's right there, Ivan. We get to the traverse and the mountain will shield us from this wind. It will be easy. Rappel down the Bottleneck and home."

His torso started to lean back. I had to pull his arm to keep him upright.

"Needle," he managed to gasp.

Five minutes of fumbling and struggle and I managed to get another syringe out and poised to inject.

"Is this dangerous?" I asked my guide.

He didn't answer. I couldn't see his eyes behind his goggles. It was getting dark. "Ivan! Ivan, is this safe?"

His hand grabbed my wrist. I could barely feel it. The mighty titan reduced to a failing centenarian.

"Do it," he said.

I pushed the needle into the thigh of his down suit and pressed the plunger. His hand clenched, a surge of crushing power, the grip of a man who lives by the strength of his will and body. I tried to pull him up with my arm but he was too heavy. His chin lifted, almost like he was trying to see behind himself to the summit. Then his torso collapsed forward towards his legs. He was still locked on my wrist as his body tipped to the side, pulling me down on top of him.

"Jesus, Ivan, come on. We gotta go!" I tried to shout. I'm not sure I was even making a sound.

No response. I couldn't free my hand from his grip.

"Get the fuck up! Goddamn you, Ivan!"

I used my teeth to pull the glove off my other hand. I pinched his frozen cheek with my fingers. I pinched and twisted.

"Wake up, Ivan. You promised – you promised!"

There was never a promise. There couldn't be promises in that place. I was panicking. I thought of Ang's wild eyes, imagined the bite of cold steel penetrating my belly, saw myself soaring through the air like Superman in a howl of wind and doom.

I released Ivan's cheek and stuffed my fingers into his neck. I pushed into the soft flesh buried beneath the layers of synthetic fabric. I couldn't find a pulse.

"You can't do this," I sobbed. "You can't leave me here alone."

I pulled my fingers out of his warmth and moved to the hand that was still squeezing my wrist. I dug past the velcro cuff to the skin beneath. No pulse in the wrist either.

"You motherfucker!" I screamed. I pounded my hand on his chest, right on the spot where duct tape held a mitten against his heart. "Get up, Ivan, get up! Get – the – fuck – up."

I was out of breath. I lay half on top of the guide. I tried to sink my consciousness down into his body, tried to feel for any movement in the ribcage – air coming in, air coming out – and then tried to will that movement into being. Reality did not obey.

I finally pushed myself into an upright, seated position. I looked for my tracks. I couldn't see them. I turned on my headlamp. The tracks were gone. The circle of light extended for thirty feet, a chaos of swirling grey, and then the wall of black began. The distant peak guiding me to the traverse had vanished in the darkness, along with the rest of the planet.

Only three things remained.

A single bubble of yellow light, a murdered man, and me.

CHAPTER TWENTY-SIX

JULY 31

I COULDN'T SLEEP. I shouldn't sleep. Go to sleep on top of K2 and you don't wake up.

The cold no longer crept through my body, it was a flood of ice in my veins. I considered getting the sat phone out of Ivan's pack. I could have called Karen. I could have called Raymond at Base, told him what happened. But instead I sat in the little pocket I'd fashioned out of the hard slope with my ice axe. I planted an ice screw into the exposed blue ice a couple of paces to my right. We were both attached to it. I couldn't bring myself to let Ivan's body slide away. I knew real mountaineers consigned their fallen comrades to the abyss but I planned on leaving him fastened to the mountain. His corpse might become famous, a landmark on the way to the summit. Yellow Jacket.

I didn't have the energy to chuckle at my gallows humour. When I shone my lamp on Ivan he no longer looked human. I couldn't see the face. Didn't want to. I'd positioned him with his back to me.

I could tell I was looking at a corpse. Was it a hardness in the back, or a rigidity in the bent legs? The onset of rigor mortis, perhaps, or the freezing process? The bottom arm was bent, like he was using it as a pillow. The gloved hand looked wrong. It was twisting on the wrist, maybe a distortion caused by freezing.

I was glad I couldn't see his face. Ice cube eyes set in a frozen expression.

I'm so sorry Ivan. I gave you an impossible temptation. It was selfish and I've killed you. Your courage and power, your wit and wisdom, reduced to a cautionary tale.

Ang was my fault, too. It had to be. The expedition existed because of my desire. The sherpa came to K2 with his best friend and then something happened. Something went wrong inside him. I felt it. I was sure Ivan felt it, too. But when it came time to make a decision, down on the traverse, I used Ang's support to blackmail Ivan. I was a self-absorbed piece of shit.

I imagined the same poisonous phrase whispered by an alien voice. I remembered the vile hunger in Varney's bulging eyes, the lewd delight in his voice as he divulged his plan to consume my bowels.

Why haven't you come to gloat? Why aren't you here, now, mocking my final moments? I raised my puffy fists to my face and punched my cheeks. Stay awake. You sleep, you die.

How much time had passed since the sun went down? It felt like four hours. Probably forty minutes. I thought about using the last syringe, but worried it might kill me. I considered searching Ivan's summit bag to see if there was anything else that could help me. The phone was in there. I could talk on the phone until the battery died. It might last an hour. Another hour that I wouldn't nod off.

I looked over at Ivan. His hand was twisted a little more. It was wrong. He was wrong. I couldn't possibly touch him. Maybe when the sun came up I'd find the courage to check the bag. But not in the dark.

Don't sleep. DO. NOT. SLEEP.

I slept.

Karen was in my dream. She was screaming at me. A warning. But her words were drowned out by the roar of an avalanche. I remained standing as it engulfed me. It buried my ex-wife but she kept yelling. White filled my world from the bottom up. Just before it swallowed my head, I figured out what she was shouting.

Yes, yes, of course!

I woke. It was Karen. She was saying something important. It was right there – if I could just…no, it was gone. I couldn't remember. Probably nothing: profound in a dream state, incoherent in the light of day.

Light of day would have been nice. I was definitely not asleep but it was pitch black. My eyes were frozen shut inside my goggles. I lifted my mittens again. I couldn't feel any of the fingers on my left hand. My right hand was throbbing. I ground my hands against the bottom of the goggles then clumsily scraped at my eyes and dislodged whatever frozen crud had sealed them.

Orange glow. Dawn rising in the east. The sun hadn't crested the peaks on the horizon but the whole sky was transforming: midnight blue in the west sliding to pastel then citrus overhead.

A cough to my right. I looked at my guide's frozen corpse. A sound, the rasp of air. Then movement. Ivan's hand, the crooked hand, it twitched.

It wasn't possible. Not a chance. Punctured, frozen, suffocated. Yet somehow moving. Hope surged in my chest and warmth cascaded down the back of my skull.

"Ivan?"

I didn't recognize the sound of my own voice. When did I last drink water? Any water on either of us would be long since frozen, and neither of us had a stove.

His head raised off the ice then fell back.

"Phil."

Ivan sounded worse than me. He sounded great for a dead man, however.

Somehow I needed to stand. My entire body from the waist down felt frozen, hours of conduction leaching my heat into the mountain. I should have put something under my ass. I checked that my feet were well planted, my crampons digging into the hard surface, and that I had a firm grip on my ice axe with my right hand. I pushed with the axe and flexed with my thighs as I leaned forward. It was easier to stand than expected. I'd thought my bucket seat in the ice was deeper. It was a wonder I hadn't slipped out while I dozed.

I chunked my feet over to Ivan.

"I'm here," I croaked, "I'm here."

"Christ almighty," he said. It was barely more than a whisper. The air was still. Had the wind dropped while I slept?

I circled below his prone body and forced my legs back up two steps.

God, his face. His nose was black. Not blue or purple, but black like the ashes of burned paper. His eyes look pretty good, though – red puffy tissue reduced to slits, sure – but there was recognition in his gaze, even alertness.

"Shit, oh shit. Your hands."

The words escaped my mouth. His gloves, both of them, had twisted almost one-eighty. His hands were backwards.

In a grim act of ventriloquism his white lips were almost motionless as he spoke.

"Must have…I don't know. Don't hurt, though. I can still use my hands. I think I can."

It made no sense. He must have balled up his hands into fists and the gloves had spun around. I dropped to one knee.

"Let me look," I said.

I touched a glove and squeezed. The hand was right there beneath the fabric, the fingers extended. It wasn't possible: how could his hands be facing the wrong direction?

"I think your wrists are broken maybe," I said. "They don't hurt?"

His head barely moved when he shook it.

I asked if he could sit up.

"I think so."

I winced as he placed his left hand on the ice and pushed. For a moment nothing happened – I certainly couldn't lift him – but then he started to rise into a seated position.

"Good thinking," he said, giving the rope attaching him to the ice screw a little pull with his twisted right hand. The wool mittens stuffed in the holes of his yellow jacket were black balls of bloody ice.

"Mind if I call you Beck Weathers?" I said to my guide.

He coughed, the closest he could get to a chuckle I supposed.

Weathers, the Everest '96 survivor, collapsed when he was lost in a blizzard on the South Col. The next day he pulled a Lazarus and stumbled into camp. I didn't believe in miracles but I'd read the books and considered the expert opinions. Like Ivan, Beck had no business being alive.

It took another five minutes for Ivan to stand. I was exhausted just from pulling on his arm. His grip felt strong, though. I couldn't imagine how that could be – and with his wrist a mess – but it was very good news. He'd need his hands to descend.

The guide insisted on taking the lead.

"We'll rope up," he said.

I didn't think either of us could stop a fall but I still took some mental comfort from the connection. The snow slope dropped steeply below us. I pointed out the distant peak I'd been using to direct myself down to the traverse.

"I know where I'm going," he said. No hostility in the tone, maybe a bit of humour. It was a good sign.

The effort of catching myself with each descending step was exhausting. My thigh muscles were completely dead. I gripped the head of my ice axe with what little strength remained in my hand and hoped I didn't collapse.

I should have *felt* something. There was no sense of horror at what had happened and no joy at the return of Ivan. I was glad Ivan was alive. Of course I was. But I didn't feel it. I stumbled down in an emotionless haze.

Almost. There was one feeling that did register. A surprising new certainty. I didn't want to die on the mountain. A death sentence gave me the courage to come to K2, but I didn't want to stay.

The mountain could still kill me, certainly, but even though I'd have to battle for every breath and fight for every metre of descent, I wanted to survive. A moment might arrive when I chose to cross a train platform, kneel, and place my neck on a rail in front of an oncoming wheel, but that would be saved for when life held no prospect but misery. Dying just because I said I would? That would be stupid. No, I'd die back home. Maybe on a train platform, maybe on a ludicrously-fast motorcycle, or maybe just whacked-out on good drugs in a hospital bed. But having a modest little tombstone, a flat one that vanished when the grass was long, suited me better than an eight-thousand metre monument. I still had time to skydive, get in my first-ever fistfight, and be rejected by a hottie in a nightclub. There was still time for life.

I could see Karen one last time.

Besides, I had to go down. A successful summit without a safe descent would be an expedition with a caveat. Making it off the mountain after the near-death of a partner and a bivouac above eight thousand metres would be legendary.

The slope was steepening. I could see where it appeared to drop off completely. That had to be the spot. It lined up with the mountain I'd used as a guide. The sun had broken free of its mountain tethers. It was still close to the horizon, the celestial body's size made manifest by its proximity to the puny features of Earth.

"It's a good day," I whispered aloud to myself.

"It is," Ivan called over his shoulder.

The air remained still but clouds covered the Godwin-Austen Glacier below. The predicted storm was coming. I wanted to ask Ivan if it would hit before we were back to Four but I didn't. It would or it wouldn't.

The guide faced forward. I started sidestepping. The snow was a little stiff from the frigid night. Coming down at the end of the day would have been a nightmare. Snow would have shed off the ice underneath like powder, a scary ride down to the traverse with no guarantee of a stop when you got there.

Every third step I slipped for a foot or more before snow compacted enough to stop me. The slope had to be seventy degrees. Ivan kept tooling down. He was sliding as much as stepping. I had to speed up to avoid the rope growing taut between us.

Storm clouds churned half a kilometre below.

"Slow down, Ivan," I called ahead.

He gave no indication he'd heard. There was certainly no change in his speed. I wanted to turn into the slope and crawl down backwards but I'd never keep up that way.

"Slow down, Ivan!" I yelled.

He looked back and smiled. His black nose, crispy ashes, looked like a strong breeze could carry it away.

"It's too fast for me, man," I said, finally having his attention.

He pointed to the left with one of his backwards hands.

"We're here, Phil. We made it."

The traverse. Twenty metres from him was an ice screw with a rope attached. The line traveled horizontally away from us. All I could see from my vantage point was the cloud-filled void. We'd made it. Fixed ropes and then an easy snow ascent would see us back to Four.

The Bottleneck could still choose to kill us but my fear was never really about K2's objective hazards, not mostly anyway. Yes, I dreaded avalanches and freezing to death, being crushed beneath a serac or swallowed by a crevasse. Even more, though, I worried about fucking up, about causing my own death – which I almost had, of course, and more than once. But now survival was possible, even likely.

If fate was on my side, I'd be drinking hot tea and eating delicious cup-noodle before darkness fell again.

CHAPTER TWENTY-SEVEN

JULY 31

THE STORM WAS climbing K2. The entire shoulder beneath us was hidden. Dense, black clouds scudded past just a few hundred metres below our feet. I knew we couldn't stay put – we were still too high, and the storm would swallow us regardless – but dropping into the maelstrom enveloping Camp Four looked like a death sentence.

"We'll be fine," Ivan shouted.

Confidence is contagious, sure, but Ivan's enthusiasm reeked of dishonesty or maybe just madness, especially given his appearance. The nose. Honestly, I had to choke back the taste of sick in the back of my throat. The tip of his black nose was completely gone. He'd never look right again.

Ivan moved over to the traverse rope and clipped in. He waved at me to follow. I faced into the slope and sidestepped to where the fixed rope began. I could feel the snow collapsing under each step. I kept waiting for it to let go completely and drop me down the rocky face until only my lifeline hooked onto Ivan saved me. I clipped a carabiner onto the traverse rope and unhooked from Ivan. I felt slightly more safe.

The guide started walking face-forward in the direction of the Bottleneck. I couldn't imagine doing the same. The drop-off looked vertical, but it was more than just topography: I saw malevolent intent in its steepness, a force trying to suck me down into oblivion. I faced into the wall of ice and stepped sideways under the giant, overhanging glacier.

Gotta breathe.

My throat felt like I'd been gargling glass. My chest ached as if a wrecking bar had been used to pry my ribs apart. Every breath was an agony. I peered down at the black hole swirling under my feet. Hard to imagine there were people ten thousand feet below me. The storm looked like liquid metal.

"Check this out," Ivan yelled.

I squinted into the wind, followed his pointing, backwards hand. There were three splashes of bright colour at the top of the Bottleneck, at the end of the traverse.

"What are they doing?"

I said the words under my breath but Ivan heard.

"That's Italy," said Ivan. "What's-his-face Stefano and a couple of their HAPs."

Surely they weren't trying to summit? It was suicide in this weather, and too late in the day regardless.

Ivan waved. I lifted my right arm, too. A figure in a blue suit raised an ice axe.

A blast of air hammered into me. I sagged against the ice wall, draping my frozen arm over the rope. The day was still bright where we were standing, the ice like glossy plastic as it reflected the deep blue of the space sky and the white light of the sun.

Two of the climbers waited at the Bottleneck, but the third, the one in blue, clipped onto the traverse and started edging towards us.

"This will be fun," said Ivan, which I didn't understand. Then I remembered. How could I have forgotten? The last time we saw the Italians one of their climbers was badly hurt. Surely they blamed us.

"You don't think…," I started.

Ivan looked back. His face was unconcerned – horribly disfigured, sure, but not in a concerned way.

"Nah," he said.

What I was wondering – what my paranoid brain was picking away at – was the notion that the Italians were back for some kind of revenge. The idea was ludicrous. There *was* that incident on Everest some years back, however, when a group of sherpas attacked a trio of climbers. And also, oh yeah, Ang.

Add passion to hardship, mix in a little oxygen deprivation, and people can get squirrelly.

"What if he died?" I said.

Ivan shook his head.

"I helped them out," he said. "I talked to Stefano myself."

Ivan kept walking. I followed a few feet behind him. What choice did I have? If the Italian climber cut the traverse rope, Ivan might manage to catch himself but I'd be gone. My life was in the hands of a stranger.

We were a hundred feet from the top of the Bottleneck when we met.

"You get the summit? Where's number three, the sherpa?" the Italian shouted.

Ivan faced away from me. I could just make out his words: "We did, but he didn't make it."

"Looks like it was tricky for you, too," said the Italian in possibly the biggest understatement I'd ever heard. Trust a mountaineer to downplay a missing nose and two blood popsicles oozing from someone's chest.

"Bit of an epic but I'll be fine," Ivan replied, as if it was a battle to see who could be more stoic. They both sounded nuts to me.

Stefano leaned his head out to get a glimpse of me.

"I saw a headlamp last night," he said. "Thought I'd come up this morning and see if I could help. These gentlemen volunteered to join me." He looked back at his colleagues.

Not here to murder us for injuring his friend. The relief was tangible, a physical sensation. I felt humbled and grateful.

"Thank you," I said. I waved at the HAPs, still waiting at the top of the Bottleneck, and got two waves in return.

"We should go," said Stefano.

It was bizarre how close the storm was to our position. It felt like we were walking on a glass floor with a hurricane raging beneath it. The darkness roiled like a witch's cauldron. The prospect of descending into it was terrifying.

Stefano led the final hundred feet of the traverse. Ivan followed and I followed Ivan. The path became slightly less steep. I risked walking forward instead of side-stepping. I looked to my right. Broad Peak was across the valley. Its upper slopes were orange in the midday light, while its lower flanks were submerged in black cloud.

One of the HAPs was staring at Ivan – it was probably hard not to look – but the other smiled at me. Stefano said something I couldn't hear. Ivan turned to me.

"I'll sweep," he said, meaning he'd bring up the rear.

Top of the Bottleneck. The Pakistani climbers went first, followed by their Italian teammate. I clipped onto the fixed line and stared down into the darkness. I could see the line for about thirty metres before visibility reduced to zero.

"Don't unclip at the bottom," Ivan yelled at me, "not until I get there. We'll rope up for the walk to Camp Four."

I nodded. Fear rode shotgun on my shoulder. I thought I'd be able to relax for the final stretch. Instead I felt the most frightened I'd been since the summit. The storm looked powerful enough to sweep me off the slope.

I'm on a fixed line. Safe for now, at least.

I started rapping down the Bottleneck. There was a clear line marking where the storm began. Bright sunlight vanished as I passed into the black. Gale-force winds lashed out, buffeting me on the line. I was thrown off-balance. My helmet struck something hard, an exposed rock perhaps, and then I was upright again. Streams of twinkling light cascaded across my vision before being absorbed into the darkness.

I looked up. I couldn't see Ivan. Nothing was visible beneath me, either, except a short length of fixed rope thrumming in the wind. I kept rapping down, barely hopping. In calm weather I could have descend the Bottleneck in big bounces, flying free of the slope as I let ten or more metres of rope pass through my gloves. But with a frozen hand and wind gusting over a hundred kilometres per hour, it took courage just lifting a crampon from the security of being attached to the ice.

The noise was deafening. I kept my face hunched between my shoulders. I wondered if the wind was strong enough to pluck off my goggles. My right foot landed on exposed rock. The crampon slipped like a skate. I toppled but I didn't hit the slope. The wind took me. I was airborne for a full two seconds before I fell back to earth. My shoulder crunched into the sheet of ice coating the couloir. The wind was knocked out of my tortured lungs.

A steel claw demolished the verglas inches from my face. The crampon was attached to Ivan's boot. He'd caught up to me. A hand gripped me under the armpits and lifted me back on my feet. I could barely make out the silhouette of my guide. There was no point trying to yell over the shriek of the wind. I could have screamed in his ear and I doubt it would have registered.

I didn't know how we'd reach Four when we got to the bottom of the Bottleneck. We'd put in a lot of work just to die a few hundred metres from our tents.

I tried to make my legs move with quick precision. I was twenty hours of effort beyond being able to do that. Somehow my descent continued, though, frozen feet and hands executing movements that had been foreign to me just months ago but now had become my entire universe.

Get to the bottom. Wait for Ivan. Get to the bottom.

I thought about seracs above us. Had the storm climbed high enough to be tearing at the face of the overhanging glacier? I imagined a great chunk of ice – a berg the size of a Greyhound bus – dropping five hundred feet onto the top of my thin helmet. The end would be instant.

Maybe that would be better. It was exhausting not giving up. Why couldn't I just give up? I'd been strong for weeks. Couldn't I just give myself a break? My left hand was dead or dying. My toes wouldn't survive. I was still days from ABC.

I hate my body, I hate my brain. Just quit.

Nope. Couldn't do it. I kept fighting. I reached the end of the first rope, which meant I was a third of the way down. Then, an hour or decade later, I reached the end of the second. Two-thirds.

The storm's ferocity had increased. The incline lessened, which was good, but the gully was shallower and provided less cover. The gale tore across the mountain face.

The rope hauled me off my feet. I slammed into the slope. Somehow I maintained a grip on my ice axe but I had to let go of the rappelling rig. I didn't slip – deadman safety catch – but could do nothing to stop the wind crushing me into the steep ice. I tried to suck down air and gather strength to fight back.

I couldn't remember if there was a fixed rope between camp and the foot of the Bottleneck. Ivan had said something about it. I couldn't recall. I couldn't remember my living room, either, or the name of my favourite restaurant. I didn't know if it was fatigue or cold, dehydration or the tumour. The world had shrunk. There was me, there was ice and there was fear.

I couldn't stay there. I had to go down swinging. I managed to get my knees beneath me. I pressed my frozen paw against the ice chute. The hand gave me no pain. With my other arm I planted the axe. I waited for the slightest lull in the air current and got one foot under me. My thighs didn't feel like part of me anymore. My body didn't feel like part of me. I had become a little pocket of awareness hunkered in a bone cave peering out through two narrowing entrances.

The eyes squeezed shut, the legs flexed and I rose to my feet.

At some point in time I reached the end of the third line. The slope eased to about thirty degrees. The fixed rope came to an end. Another climber was waiting there.

I recognized Stefano by the colour of his jacket. He was sitting with his back to me, still clipped to the same line I was on. He was only six feet away but the roaring wind had concealed my approach. I stumbled a step closer and reached out a hand for his shoulder.

Just before I touched him it occurred to me he might be dead. Maybe he was frozen solid. Maybe even his clothing was frozen, like he was a statue carved from ice.

The shoulder gave under pressure from my hand. His head turned ever so slightly in acknowledgment. I hunkered down and yelled at the back of his hood.

"Wait for Ivan. Any minute. Where are the HAPs?"

Stefano shook his head.

"Wait here," I said. I tried to step down beside Stefano. I lodged a crampon into the leg of his down suit, almost embedding it in his thigh. I didn't have the energy to correct it, though, and just barely controlled my fall as I slid into place beside him.

The climber leaned into me. I threw an arm around his shoulder. I tried to think about brave penguins, birds with Morgan Freeman's voice, huddled together against the Antarctic winter. I only made out every other word when Stefano spoke.

"– don't – where – HAPs – can't – camp –"

Ivan would know what to do.

It wasn't more than a few minutes before I heard his voice.

"We're gonna make it, boys," he said, his voice as clear and optimistic as a vote of confidence offered in a plush limo.

I didn't turn my head. I couldn't face the wind head on. But I nodded as much as my frozen neck allowed.

"We're gonna crawl down the Shoulder to the tents," said his voice in my left ear. I turned to speak but stopped when I saw the midnight skull that had replaced his face: the nose an open pit, the black-tipped cheeks and chin, the black goggles. I couldn't imagine how he continued to speak and move, how he continued to breathe.

"I'm tired, Ivan," I said. I didn't mean to. I was supposed to say something positive and absurd. Truth slipped out.

"This day will end, you can be sure of that," said the guide. "It will end as soon as you stop. So make sure you stop in the right place."

"The right place," I parroted.

"The right place," said Stefano.

Ivan snapped a carabiner onto my harness. The rope extended from me to Stefano. The wind had turned. It was blasting uphill. Gravity wasn't strong enough to counter its force. The Ukrainian circled around us as calmly as you stroll up to a grill for another hot dog. Then he hunkered down on all fours and started pulling downhill.

Ivan swung his axe and planted the pick. He kicked the front points of a crampon into the ice and pushed. The short-rope pulled taut. His effort, plus the mass of a planet, were enough to pull us a foot in the direction of Camp Four, about half a kilometre down and a kilometre across from us.

I bent over from my seated position and swung my axe. Throwing my arm against the wind was exhausting, but the steel point bit into the slope. By the time I counted ten swings my shoulder was screaming. My back joined the chorus a few crampon kicks after that. I could just make out Ivan ahead of me. I don't know how he knew what direction to go – downhill, of course, but downhill led to lots of places less welcoming than Camp Four. Choose the wrong direction and we'd propel ourselves right off the edge of vertical cliffs.

Would the tents even be there when we arrived in camp? It was hard to imagine any structure, never mind one made of fabric, surviving the storm.

Ivan rose to his feet. He leaned into the gale and kept moving forward. I raised one hand off the ice – the left hand, the frostbitten one the docs would likely have to saw off my arm if I lived long enough – and the wind immediately took me. It lifted my torso and threatened to throw me backwards. Only my grip on the ice axe with my right hand, the pick driven three inches into the slope, kept me planted.

I pulled with an effort I didn't know I could still muster and managed to flatten my body to the ground. The taut rope pulled uncomfortably on my groin, the harness cinching up around my waist. My already-straining lungs were compressed further. I was yanked forward.

Ivan was dragging me.

I kicked with my crampons and tried to keep pace. I had energy in bursts of five seconds. Between bursts, as I gasped and suffered, Ivan pulled my limp carcass down the ice. The rope connecting me to Stefano was taut. Ivan pulled us both.

The blizzard was apocalyptic. My guide vanished in the white. I looked back. Stefano was gone, too. Visibility was reduced to an arm's length. I couldn't even make out the tip of my axe as I swung it. My face no longer burned with cold. I'd frozen it. Ivan and I would end up twins if I was out much longer.

Another yank on the rope. Another. Then a steady pull that built up speed.

I tried to scramble with my feet – tried to participate at least symbolically – but we were moving too fast. It occurred to me we were still going downhill, which wasn't as obvious as it might seem in disorienting, whiteout conditions. Ivan was racing forward, hopefully towards a tent. If it was a precipice, I wouldn't know until I was in the air.

The wind was stronger. A hundred and fifty? I had no idea. Ivan was fighting for every foot. Or maybe fighting wasn't the right word, not at the speed I was being pulled. I felt like a child on an outing with his mom, sitting in a toboggan as she strode down a frozen sidewalk. Stefano had given up, as well. I could tell by the pressure around my waist he was contributing nothing to our progress.

I couldn't imagine Ivan's strength. As an armchair mountaineer, I'd read some incredible stories, some of them right on K2. The "miracle belay" during the first American expedition took place not far from where we were. The sport's top performers regularly exceeded what sounded possible. Gerlinde Kaltenbrunner and her teammates jetted up from K2 basecamp to the top of the shoulder—and back down again—in less than forty hours, a climb and descent of more than 3,000 vertical metres each way.

Ivan's performance was beyond comprehension, however. Climbers don't get stronger at 8,000 metres. You bring your strength with you from the world below and then it gets stripped away until you die.

But remember Beck Weathers, and not just him. Wilco van Rooijen survived the 2008 disaster on K2. He wasn't the only survivor, sure, but he was the only one who went down the wrong part of the mountain, snow-blind, and descended off-route until he somehow found Camp Three. He spent two full nights exposed on the mountain. Doug Scott on Baintha Brakk, the Ogre: broke both his legs just below the summit, at around seven-thousand metres, and crawled down with his team through a snowstorm.

Miracles aren't miracles. They aren't luck, they aren't supernatural. Ivan was a machine because he'd spent his entire life becoming one. Of course he could walk through a hurricane, of course he could survive paltry stab wounds, of course he could save two lives all by himself. He was Ivan the Terrible, cover boy of Sender magazine and bona fide action hero.

Some reserve of something – not energy, exactly, more like crankiness – stirred in my gut, down in my long-empty stomach. I started working again. My crampons gripped the mountainside and I pushed off.

Snow was accumulating at an astonishing rate, despite the wind, only increasing my amazement that Ivan could pull me and Stefano. I had to help. I pumped my knees and got my arms moving in time. The tension connecting me to Ivan eased up ever so slightly, although this left me with a larger share of the burden pulling Stefano. After a few seconds, though, the pressure from the Italian eased, too. Stefano started helping as well.

I tried to imagine the courage it took the Italian to leave Camp Four and head up the Bottleneck on a rescue mission to help men you blamed for wiping out one of your own teammates. And the HAPs. One of their colleagues was killed beside me when I refused to leave the fixed line.

I wouldn't rescue me. Stefano's altruism and the kindness of the HAPs were so extreme they defied comprehension. Maybe I needed to make some changes, actually start giving a shit about someone other than myself. I didn't have a lot of time left to do it. It might be nice to join the human race before I left it.

Had the wind dropped? Maybe. Or perhaps what I was feeling was hope. I was shattered. I felt far worse than I thought a person *could* feel and still be alive. But I also felt sure I wouldn't stop. Not until the wind froze me solid and the mountain smashed me into splinters.

I needed to phone Karen. I hadn't spoken to her once. It was so easy on the mountain to focus on reducing myself to particles in motion. Flesh and bone. Physics and nothing else. Feeling emotions was hard. Thoughts betray you. When the task at hand was so simple – move – any energy devoted to sentiment was strength lost.

And yet...

...take the heart out of what I was doing – eliminate emotion – and there was no point. Just molecules moving. Only thought makes things matter.

I needed to call Karen. I couldn't shut myself off, not even if thought led to fear and fear led to despair. Caring might be dangerous, even lethal. Courage means more than staring down a cliff face, however. I had just moments left on Earth – weeks if I was lucky, seconds if I wasn't – and somehow I had to find the strength to give a shit about the very thing I was on the cusp of losing.

Fail that test and I'd just be a stone buried under a rock.

Chapter Twenty-Eight

IVAN FOUND OUR tent.

I don't know how. I'd thought the storm was letting up but I was wrong. Visibility had gone from terrible to impenetrable. It was like trying to scuba dive in milk. Very cold milk that wanted to kill you.

Ivan pulled me close. He stank, a nasty, familiar smell I couldn't place. It had to be coming from that black gash on his face where he used to have a nose.

"We're here," he said. Somehow his voice was calm and quiet, a neat trick with the hurricane klaxon of the storm muting everything else to white noise.

Ivan placed my right hand on the nylon shell of the tent. The tiny shelter bucked with the force of the wind. I hunkered down and used the structure as a meager windbreak. I pulled on the rope connecting me to Stefano. I struggled for what felt like ten minutes but I'm sure was much less. I turned to ask for Ivan's help but he was gone, presumably in the tent.

"Ivan, help! Ivan!"

No response, or none that I could hear. I kept pulling. I wondered if I was going to have a coronary. My sides ached after so many hours with a radically elevated resp rate.

You're going to die out here. You're trying to return a favour and it's going to kill you.

I squashed the thought. I pulled and pulled. I didn't know how my feeble effort was having an effect, but the rope was coming one foot at a time.

I didn't know Stefano had arrived until I felt something touch my boot. I was completely blind. Forget swimming in milk. The storm hammered me like a bird strike, as if I was in the cockpit of a jet that had flown into a flock of geese, ten-pound lumps of white feathers exploding around me, into me, at hundreds of miles per hour.

I leaned forward with my good hand. It only took a moment to realize I was touching the top of his helmet.

I moved down, searching for his face. I found something unfamiliar. Something jagged. I yanked my hand back.

"Ivan!" I yelled. "Stefano!"

No response from either. I stooped forward onto my hands and knees and shuffled closer to the Italian. I found his helmet again and then the jagged spot. I followed the rough edge and it dropped off. I could feel a nylon strap. Was it the side? Why didn't it feel more familiar?

My hand was off the helmet. I pulled it closer and touched hair. I ran my fingers forward, looking for the front of his face. Was that his nose? I found the jagged part of the helmet again. No, no, no – the helmet was torn, smashed, something – and then the confusing surfaces and spaces beneath it.

Jesus, it had to be Stefano's face. It had to be what was left of his face.

"Stefano! Ivan, goddammit, I need your help!"

It couldn't be as bad as it felt. I was disoriented, half crazy. I felt around under the helmet, searching for hair again. I found some but then it unexpectedly ended in a pocket, a crater of some kind. I yanked back my hand. Did I just cram my fingers into his mouth? His mouth was on the other side, wasn't it?

I was freezing to death but I had to know. My left hand was history. I couldn't have been more than two metres from shelter but I didn't know if I had the strength left to cover that gap and save myself. It was the end of me, my absolute limit, but I forced myself to lean towards Stefano until my goggles touched his helmet. I saw the electric blue of its shell. My headlamp was still working. I hadn't been sure.

I slid my face towards the jagged part of Stefano's helmet. My chin scratched on it. I used that numb sensation to guide my goggles down to the part I was sure had shattered.

I couldn't make sense of what I was seeing. I knew what I should be seeing. I was looking where Stefano's face was supposed to be. Instead, there was frozen red, icy white and grey-pink slush.

Blood, bone and brains.

I pulled my face back and fell on my ass in the deepening snow. I felt like I was still moving, riding surging swells on a turbulent ocean. My heart rate was through the roof, each contraction a stab radiating through my ribcage.

When did it happen? Was it a rock, maybe a chunk of ice? I was sure he'd been moving on his own power. He was helping as I struggled to reel him in. How could I have dragged his frozen body to the tent in my weakened state?

Stefano was gone. Everything dies here.

Not me, though. Not yet. I found the tent, then the zipper. I didn't have the strength or dexterity to remove my crampons. I opened the flap, stepped in and collapsed in a pile of spindrift and crusty sleeping bags.

157

I had to zip the tent back up to prevent it from tearing or filling like a parachute and lifting us right off the shoulder. The thought of moving made me want to weep.

"Ivan," I said. I didn't have the energy to yell.

The guide didn't answer. I rocked my body, trying to find his, but felt nothing.

I had to zip up the tent. Snow was blasting in. I searched for the zipper with my good hand. I couldn't find it. Then I did find it. I pulled and pulled. My muscles felt like they were becoming unmoored from my bones. I didn't want to die.

I closed my eyes.

A blast of arctic air. Did the flap open again? Did I leave it open? A presence blocked the wind. The sound of the zipper. A body beside me, moving. I pushed towards it, a hamster seeking warmth where there could be none.

I could feel the mountain through the floor of the tent. The ice creaked. I woke to a rumble of distant avalanches. Then I jolted awake to the bucking of an avalanche much closer, so close it felt like the tent must be buried. I could do nothing. The world shook and I waited to see what would happen. I fell asleep before getting an answer.

I dreamt of Varney. He was stomping his hobnailed boots into Stefano's face. The Italian's head collapsed like a rotten melon. "Now his face is even uglier than mine," said Varney. The creature was wrong, though. Stefano's mashed face looked like gooey pizza – it *was* gooey, deep dish pizza – but the menace in the monster's bulging eyes and round gash of a mouth was the most terrible thing I could imagine. An ice axe was in each of my frozen hands, the tools curved black and chitinous. I could plant them right in Varney's rotten face and twist, see if his head spilled pizza toppings, too.

"Phil, wake up. It's morning."

Ang had brought coffee. No, Ang was gone. Ang killed Ivan and then he flew away.

"The sun is up, sort of," said the voice. Not Ivan.

I opened my eyes.

I was wrong, it *was* Ivan. He sat beside me in the tent, hunched over to avoid getting wet from the condensation beading on the inside of the bowed fabric.

"Are we buried?" I asked.

He chuckled. Good spirits.

"A foot maybe. No big deal."

Stefano.

"The Italian," I said. "He's outside. I called you."

"I didn't hear you. I went to check on the others."

I felt anger towards Ivan. It was baseless. I'd have been dead ten times over if it weren't for him. He got me to the tent and still had the energy to look for others at Camp Four.

"How many are there?"

"Just one tent. The climber with the busted leg and a HAP."

I was shocked. The rest of the Italian expedition abandoned their teammates?

"What about Stefano and the HAPs with him?" I asked. "No tents were left for them?"

Ivan said three tents, including Ang's, were swept away just after the storm struck.

"...just vaporized, according to Mohammed. He was poking his head out of his tent, to see if someone had more painkillers for his patient. Avalanche broke loose just above camp, carried away the three tents beside him. Whole team is gone. The guy's a mess."

I asked how the Italian with the broken leg was doing.

"Just waiting to die. It would be a mercy to send him on his way."

What did Ivan just say?

"And there's no sign of the HAPs who came up the Bottleneck for us," he continued. "Storm got them, too, I guess."

"You seem very calm about this," I said.

Ivan's face didn't change much. No frown. The faintest hint of a bemused smile, actually.

"Am I supposed to wail and gnash my teeth?" he said. "Freaking out will improve this situation somehow? You know me better than that."

I thought I did know him better than that. He was focused to a fault, sure, and would never indulge hand-wringing. But was this the same man who wanted to abandon our summit attempt to help an injured climber? The same man who wanted to cancel pressing on to Camp Three to help one of our sherpas down to Camp Two?

Snow cascaded into the tent when Ivan cracked the zipper. It was dark in the tent because we were covered in snow, but it was also gloomy outside. The wind had died down completely. Snow was still falling steadily, though. I followed Ivan to the flap as he climbed out. I passed him a collapsible shovel.

He stomped out of view, revealing the white mound that was Stefano. Was the Italian a sterling example or a warning? Was it still heroic if you failed? We celebrate heroes who succeed. The ones who fail are forgotten, even if they made the ultimate sacrifice. Ivan was the one who got us down. Stefano was dead, and so, presumably, were the HAPs who helped him. Was it just pointless then? Three dead trying to rescue a guide who didn't need their help and a client who's terminally ill.

The cold had eased a little. I couldn't feel my left hand. I was too scared to remove my mitten and look at it. My toes were burning, which was surprising: still some nerve activity in the foot.

Ivan made short work of shovelling off the tent.

"I'm gonna check on Italy," he said.

I could just make out the remaining Italian tent. It was white, a low lump a hundred feet away. I looked back at Stefano's smaller white lump.

He'd be down the mountain in a few years. A bit here, a bit there, locked in the glacier. Reduced to a charnel smell in the nostrils of trekkers scrambling up to the Gilkey Memorial to meditate on the magnificent madness of mountaineering.

There was a flash of movement. Beyond Stefano, in the direction of the Bottleneck.

Was it Varney reappearing after all the excitement had passed? I saw two dark, vertical smudges in the monochromatic landscape. They were standing still, except for the staccato effect created by the rapid hail of icy sleet.

"Hello?" I yelled.

I wasn't sure I'd seen anything. Shadows. My imagination.

"Hello?" I shouted again. I stood up in the tent's entrance and waved my hands. I stepped out, passing carefully around Stefano's white blanket, and walked forward ten paces.

Who could still be out there? Survivors from the avalanche that swept Camp Four? The HAPs, the ones that accompanied Stefano? Surely not. They couldn't have survived the previous night exposed. No human could.

I called and waved my arms. My orange shell jacket was as visible as anything could be in the grey-white landscape. I wished I had a flare. I had a whistle in my large pack marooned at Base Camp amidst a sea of reporters and cameramen. Probably already found by a journalist, fuel to keep the 24-hour news cycle pedalling. I could imagine the pundits, whistle experts opining on the advantages of yellow plastic over green or parsing my decision to leave such a critical piece of gear behind while I clambered to my doom.

There was no one out there in the snow. Of course there wasn't. It was like thinking you saw someone out the porthole of a submarine. I walked back to the tent. The snow was deep, mid-thigh in spots. The load on the slope down to Camp Three from the Shoulder would be immense. Prime avalanche conditions. Shit.

I didn't want to die that way. I was okay, relatively speaking, with the notion of being knocked unconscious and then dismembered. But what if the avalanche didn't kill you? Being buried alive had to be one of the worst ways to go.

Take a breath, Phil. A shallow, wheezing breath. *Now* is what exists.

The past was gone, the future would never come. I was standing on a gentle grade outside a tent. I'd survived a bivouac in the death zone and achieved something amazing along the way. I'd stood atop K2. I'd succeeded. That was something, wasn't it?

But what about Ang and Stefano?

I couldn't think about that. I'd think later. I needed to live. I needed to get off the mountain and see Karen.

Ivan was coming out of the other tent carrying two canisters of fuel.

"They had extra," said Ivan.

More fuel was always good. We could be trapped on the Shoulder for a while. No fuel, no hydration, no life.

"What's the plan?" I asked.

Ivan raised his chin to the sky.

"We wait."

I asked him how the other two were doing.

"The HAP is better. I told him we'll go down when the storm breaks. He's good with that."

"And Broken Leg?"

I immediately regretted my cruel nickname and casual tone. The guide shook his head.

"Barely conscious. He won't make it."

Ivan told us, right after the accident on the traverse: There was one chance to save the man, but it would mean abandoning our summit aspirations. Did I do the wrong thing? By the usual moral measures, sure. I was definitely selfish. The man's situation was not my fault, however. If he hadn't been a self-entitled, belligerent ass, I never would have provoked him. Even then, he could have used a bit of common sense and waited until we were off the traverse before staging a confrontation. He made the wrong choice and wrong choices get you killed, full stop. I could pretend to myself I regretted what happened on summit day but I didn't *feel* it.

All I felt was tired.

"Ivan, what happened up there?"

I didn't know I was going to ask the question before the words came out.

I didn't look at the guide's face, the black pit where his nose used to be. I looked at his hands instead. His backwards hands were a horror show but at least gloves covered them.

"He fell," said my companion. "He lost his shit and he fell."

"I'm not talking about him," I said back. "With Ang. Why did he do that?"

The nasal crater in Ivan's face had become smooth, the rotting black flesh scoured away by wind and ice. Skeletor was my guide.

"I don't know. Why do you think?" he said.

I didn't expect that answer. I stumbled trying to think of a response. He filled the silence.

"He said he was trying to save his kid. Maybe he was. I have no idea how killing me on K2 would help his son back in Kathmandu. But maybe it would have. If he'd finished me and murdered you, perhaps his son would have emerged from his illness unscathed. He'll never know, though, because he failed. He had a plan and he didn't get it done."

I was confused. What was Ivan saying?

"Did you see that, though?" he continued. "Whooosh! He really soared off the summit. Up, up and away! I wish I had a video. That was something."

I was horrified by Ivan's callousness. He misread my curled lip and squinting eyes as skepticism. He continued:

"I've spent my life in these mountains. Weird happens, okay, especially in this place. Maybe all this time Ang could actually fly. Maybe being a climber was just his secret identity. I'm all ears, though, if you've got another idea."

"I...I don't think Ang was a supervillain," I said. "I think he went crazy and the wind took him. That had to be what happened."

Ivan looked like he was going to jump on that. He caught himself instead. A small smile creased his ghastly face before he spoke in a quiet voice that slipped softly into my ear canal.

"*Had* to be, huh, no other possible explanation? Phil, do you believe in God – you know, in a world beyond this world? What I'm asking is, are you a believer?"

I had a rote answer to that question: No, definitely not. Faith was for fools. I didn't trust half of what people said to my face. Why would I believe nasty fables scratched on parchment two thousand years ago?

My faith in atheism was coming under some strain, however. It was like I was starting to see the empty spaces between the nuclei of the atoms that surrounded me. Solid wasn't as solid as I'd always believed. Ang flew off the top of a mountain after trying to murder his best friend.

Nothing made sense.

"No," I said.

Ivan nodded. He held both of his backwards hands up, like he was offering a benediction.

"And yet here I sit, stabbed, twisted and frozen, and talking to you," he said. "Listen, I get it. I've seen no evidence of the Lord's hand at work, either, at least not the kindly Santa-figure the Christ-ers are always braying about. But it's getting pretty hard to deny that wondrous things *do* happen, wouldn't you say Phil? I mean, look at me. I'm a bloody miracle."

CHAPTER TWENTY-NINE

AUGUST 4

THE SNOW HADN'T stopped. Two of us crammed into a tent at Camp Four. I felt like I was suffocating every time I woke from the delirious half-slumber that counts for sleep at that altitude.

Ivan smelled.

Mountaineers smell. It's part of the sport. You don't bathe on expeditions, at least not above Base Camp, and you don't change your clothes, either. A change of clothing is extra weight. I carried a fresh pair of socks and underwear for each day – a bit extravagant – but the same pants and shirts, even long johns, were worn day after day.

Your nose gives up. You stop smelling the stench. But I could smell Ivan. He reeked of rot, like something lurking behind the wall of jars and bottles in an over-stuffed fridge. Maybe you'd find the source under bags of vegetables and ziplocks of lunch meat. It wouldn't be a true solid, anymore, more like a slime – a greasy putrescence you'd cast into the garbage, even though you were supposed to separate compostables from plastic.

I didn't say this to Ivan. He kept his clothes on. So did I. Maybe it was his feet that were decaying, or his hands. Could the broken wrists have gone septic? His whole face looked bad, too, not just the crater that used to be his nose. He'd always been lean, but the addition of a green hue had turned him cadaverous.

"And what does the chef recommend today? Perhaps the chicken?" said Ivan. He passed me the freeze-dried pouch.

His voice was upbeat. That was the thing: he was full of energy. Judged solely on the way he was moving and the work he was accomplishing, he was in great shape. He got up four times to shovel off the tent while I stayed in my sleeping bag coughing.

It only took a few minutes to boil water from snow. Boiling temperature was lower because of the reduced air pressure at altitude. I tore open the aluminum package and dumped its contents into the pot.

We had no shortage of food. Four days we'd been waiting for the storm to let up and we had enough to last four more days at least. Suggesting tandoori chicken as an option was a joke, though. There was a mistake supplying high camp. The only dehydrated food we had left was the Indian poultry dish.

I didn't leave the tent. Not if I could help it. Stefano was still there. I asked Ivan on our second snow-bound day if we could move the dead man but the guide said it was a waste of energy. Then I asked if I could use the sat phone to call Karen. He said it was a waste of battery: "We need to save it for an emergency," as if the events that had happened so far didn't qualify.

I spooned a portion of the chicken into Ivan's cup. Cool steam rose from it. I blew on mine for a minute and then began the exhausting process of moving bite-sized portions from my own mug to my mouth.

Everything ached. My fingers hurt, every crease on my body, all the joints, all the muscles, my teeth, my nostrils (why was there always blood caked around each?) and my brain. My brain stabbed itself with slasher-movie ferocity.

I still hadn't seen the HAP or the patient. Ivan said we didn't want either of them in with us. They'd gone nuts, he said. There was no room, anyway. Barely enough space for me, Ivan, and his stench. It overpowered the curry odour of the tandoori chicken.

"Snow will let up tomorrow," he said. "You wait and see."

I tried to feel excitement. There was nothing there. My world was orange tent fabric pressing down on me, cold in the parts of my body I could still feel, and blessed numbness in the parts I couldn't.

"That's good," I said.

Bright orange eventually became dull orange. Day was ending. I ate another serving of tandoori chicken. I unzipped the tent door a couple of feet to let in some fresh air. It was freezing in the tent but even colder outside. Anything, though, to take the edge off the odour.

Maybe the stench was coming from me. I didn't have the courage to look. If I took my boot off, I'd never get it back on. The foot would swell. The toes were a loss, maybe the whole foot. The burning in my toes was gone. If I really concentrated I could feel pain around the ankle. That would be where live tissue met frozen.

I kept my hand in my glove, too. I'd seen pictures before the trip. Frostbite is ghastly. I didn't need to look at that, especially when there wasn't a damn thing I could do to treat it.

Ivan left for a few minutes then came back. He turned off his headlamp once he lay down. I was already back in my sleeping bag. We'd filled our water bottles. Both of mine were tucked in the bag to stop them from freezing.

"I'll wake you in the morning," he said. "No stars yet but the snow has stopped and the wind is down."

I asked about the other two.

"They don't want to leave," said Ivan.

"We have to insist."

"I make decisions on the mountain," he said. "Gino can't walk and there's no way you and me and one crazy HAP are going to carry him down. Just forget it, Phil. It's not on you, it's on me and I say no."

That didn't sit right with me. Stefano was frozen right outside our tent. He gave his life trying to save ours. I didn't know how much I cared about anything anymore but this seemed like an easy moral calculation to make: we should return the favour and help his teammate.

Easier said than done. I didn't know the first thing about lowering an incapacitated climber from Camp Four on K2. Ivan was the one tasked with seeing me safely down, and I didn't pay for two clients. It was his rescue to perform or not. He'd made his choice.

I tried to sleep. Maybe I succeeded. It was hard to know. Blackness when my eyes were shut, blackness when they were open.

"Phil."

It was Varney. The voice was right beside me, intimate, as if he'd wedged himself between me and Ivan.

"You're dying, Phil..."

Not news.

"...but you don't have to die."

Tell that to my tumour, I answered.

"You are not your tumour. You are not your brain," said the voice.

Yes, I am, Varney. I am my brain. And I'm pretty sure you are my brain, too, seasoned with a pinch of cancer and a just a sprinkle of oxygen-deprivation.

"Oh, Phil. You've seen my power and still you doubt. Don't worry, I won't demand faith. I will show you and then you'll understand," said the voice.

What will you show me? I waited in the dark for an answer but he was gone.

I opened my eyes in the gloom of muted dawn, just the faintest hint of orange on the nylon walls that protected me.

"Ivan," I said. "Ivan."

He grunted.

"Was I talking in my sleep?" I asked.

"Dunno. Didn't hear anything."

The guide pulled himself out of his sleeping bag. Rancid fumes assaulted my nostrils. I coughed. I felt like I was going to choke or even vomit.

166

"Good thing we're going down. You don't sound good," he said.

You smell like rotting colon, Ivan.

The guide unzipped the tent and stepped out. His down suit blocked the view but I could tell it had warmed up; no blast of Arctic frost attacked my exposed face. He turned back and pushed his face into the tent. I looked away. The skin around his ruined nose looked wrong – loose, somehow, like it might start to billow and peel.

"Yup, it looks good," he said. "We should get moving."

A strong desire to go didn't translate into anything close to actual speed. I'd never felt more tired. My heart raced as I sat up. I gasped for air as I forced down the remnants of the previous night's meal. When I exited the tent and stood up, a wave of dizziness threatened to topple me.

Stefano was barely a bump under all the snow. I didn't know how much had fallen. Metres. The slope down to Camp Three would be loaded. I figured we had a fifty-fifty chance of being avalanched.

The sky was the deep blue you get when you've left most of the atmosphere's clutter behind. I peered up at the summit. The ice cliff overhanging the Bottleneck bulged with its plastic sheen.

I'd stood on top of that place. It felt like a life ago.

"We going or what? Get your crampons on," Ivan said.

I looked over at the other tent. Our shelter was a single layer; light and quick to erect, even if it did trap moisture a bit. The Italian tent had two-layers, a fly weather-proofing the tent beneath. But the fly was barely attached. The coated fabric drifted off the back of the tent like a bride's train, lightly flapping and folding when the breeze caught it.

"Crampons, Phil," said the guide.

I bent over and snapped the spikes in place. Ivan clipped a carabiner to my harness.

"You sure those don't hurt?" I said, looking down at his backwards hands.

"Just one of those things, I guess," he answered, saying nothing.

I used my good hand to attach a second carabiner from the short-rope to my harness. One locking carabiner and one non-locking, placed in opposite directions so pressure on one side wouldn't release both at the same time.

My left leg was bad. I took a tentative step forward. I half expected it to collapse as I weighted it, but it held. I felt like I was walking with a peg leg as I slowly shuffled forward. Our route took us close to the Italian tent. I wanted to ask Ivan again. There had to be something we could do. I knew what his answer would be, though.

"Hey!" I called. "Hello in the tent?"

Ivan stopped walking.

"What are you doing?" he said.

"We have to." I didn't look at him. I cupped my hands around my mouth: "Hey, are you awake? We're going!"

The wall of the tent bulged, a body pressed against it. Then a bare hand pushed out through the zipper, followed by the sleeve of a shell jacket.

"Hold on, I'm coming," I said. I took two steps in the direction of the tent before the short-rope stopped me.

A shoulder appeared. Weight dragged down the zipper. A person collapsed through the flap and landed half out of the tent on his side. His back, facing us, heaved with the effort.

"Christ, Ivan, we've got to help."

I pulled against the taut rope, unable to move forward. The man shoved his bare hands into the snow and planted his arms. He was kicking with his legs, tearing the tent flap as he freed his lower body. The front half of the structure was collapsing by the time he managed to get his feet out. His bare feet.

"I think things may have gotten a little out of hand in the Italian tent," said Ivan.

The bare-footed man stood. Snow swallowed his legs to the knee. He turned around. It was the HAP. It had to be the HAP, right? The Italian couldn't stand, not with a mangled leg. The thing was, I couldn't make sense of the face. The hood was up, the goggles on. And there was blood.

The mouth was a red gash. Beneath it cascaded a frozen, crimson waterfall. A solid column of ice fused the mouth to the chin and the chin to the chest. The whole front of his torso was a scarlet breastplate.

"Must have improvised when he ran out of food," said my guide.

I made a sound. I didn't know what sound I was making. I'd never made it before.

I couldn't accept what I was seeing. A vile energy crackled through the air. I couldn't tell where it was coming from: the blood-soaked HAP, the terrible mystery in the tent, or somewhere else. The shattered figure raised a single arm, pointed a bare hand in our direction. It was black and rotten with cold. I took a step back. Was he about to run at me, attack me, sink his corrupted teeth into my flesh – poison me with the fevered horror show that had so clearly consumed his mind? I couldn't breathe. If I'd managed to draw breath, I would have expelled it in a scream.

The snow moved. The tent sagged, then jumped, before collapsing completely on itself. The HAP swayed but his arm didn't drop. He didn't windmill or make any effort to keep his balance as he tipped over.

"No!" I finally yelled. He fell backward into the wellspring of a new avalanche and started to slide.

It was as if a plug had been pulled in a sink. White powder disappeared beneath the HAP's feet with the orderly efficiency of an execution. There was no sound for a second and then a near-instant crescendo into a deafening roar. The tent was half-submerged as it raced downhill. I saw a stiff arm bob in the current – the HAP still pointing – before being swallowed.

A great cloud of ice pellets and water billowed up from the slopes below us. The divot where the collapse began reached almost to my feet, stopping less than a metre from my toes. Calls don't get closer.

"Dear me," said Ivan.

I didn't even process his words at first. When the absurdity of them finally dawned on me, I flushed with anger.

"What the fuck, Ivan?" I barked.

He shrugged. "Honestly, it was for the best. You saw him. What a mess. I'm not sharing a rope with that."

He was talking like a crazy person. Were it not for him being stronger than I'd ever seen him – ruined face and sickly pallor notwithstanding – I'd have assumed he had cerebral edema. Then again, maybe he *had* gone crazy: attacked by his best friend, near-death experience on the summit, days trapped in a tent.

People went crazy on mountains. People went crazy on K2.

Dudley Wolfe was on the 1939 American expedition. He got stuck alone at Camp Four for a week, and that was after already spending a week above eight thousand metres. It took two attempts for his team to reach him *but he refused to leave.* The three sherpas tasked with rescuing Wolfe went back for a final, third attempt. No one knows if they even reached him. They vanished and so did Wolfe. In 2002, a leather mitten was found at the foot of the mountain with his name sewn in it.

There was nothing to say. A sensible conversation with Ivan was clearly not possible. I was shaking. A tight feeling in the back of my throat threatened to devolve into puking.

Ang's act of betrayal and fatal flight. Stefano's crushed face. The gore-soaked HAP.

Ivan. Crazy Ivan.

I wondered if I was the one who'd gone crazy. Maybe I was hallucinating. Maybe I was still trapped on the summit. Perhaps I was in a hospital bed back in North America. Had the tumour somehow trapped me in the Matrix? The notion of climbing K2 dressed in a black leather trench coat almost evoked a smile. Almost.

There was no red pill in my pocket, however. I really was on a mountain and Ivan really must have lost his shit. Should I have been surprised, though? No one who free soloed K2's summit glacier face could be completely sane. The good news was that Ivan insane was still ten times the climber I'd ever been. As long as he wanted to keep living and I stay roped to him, I had a good chance.

We skirted the edge of the shelf where the snow released. I kept waiting for a second collapse, but it was kind of pointless; by the time I knew something was wrong, I'd already be as good as dead.

Working our way downhill was slow going. We sank into waist-deep pockets. Desperation pushed us. You'd never choose to be on a slope that steep with that much snow – especially not in daylight, when the sun weakened the chemical bonds binding the ice crystals together – but I was past asking questions. I wanted off the hill.

I hoped my left leg would warm up but it didn't happen. Apparently optimism won't revive the dead. I paused to give my overworked lungs a break. Ivan kept going. I started again so I wouldn't be dragged.

"This is hopeless," I said. Camp Four's lone remaining tent had vanished beyond the curve of the slope above us.

"Yes," said Ivan. He kept going.

I could have done anything with my final weeks on Earth. Camped out in a brothel in Vegas. Volunteered with the Red Crescent in Yemen. Injected opioids – I even had a prescription – and discovered if the junkies had it right all along. I picked K2.

I looked at Ivan's back. I studied his twisted hands. I didn't know how someone's wrist bones could get switched up like that, not unless they were broken. But surely he couldn't use his hands if they were hitched to broken bones?

Mind over matter. I'd read about a retired Navy SEAL who ran an ultramarathon on a broken foot. Then there's that famous photo on the cover of Rage Against the Machine's first album: a cross-legged monk sitting calmly in a Saigon intersection as he's consumed by fire.

Ivan wasn't human like me. Some people are just better. They become rock stars and astronauts, they run marathons in two hours and invent atom bombs. I was just a schmoe. My greatest claim to fame was being the subject of a single joke in a single late-night TV monologue, some throwaway about radiation treatments and the thin atmosphere on top of mountains. I never saw the clip but Raymond tried to describe it to me. The head porter had bad comedic timing.

The avalanche debris field widened. The curve of the slope finally revealed the location of Camp Three. I saw a tiny fleck of orange on the vast white. Our tent was just to the right of where the avalanche barrelled through. It peaked out from the ledge the sherpas carved out of the slope, a little pod of civilization in the wilderness.

"How far today?" I said.

"Camp Two probably. We'll see," Ivan called over his shoulder.

The Black Pyramid would be easier in reverse. We could rappel all the way down, assuming our fixed lines were still in place.

Another hour. You think you can only walk so far, but that distance is less than ten percent of what you can really do. Here's what's crazy: some people survived the Nazi concentration camps. We've all seen the pictures. Walking skeletons. You can imagine their heartbeats visible through their denuded chests. Even when your brain thinks you're done, your body isn't close. Billions of mindless cells that want to keep moving.

Live. Live. Live. Live.

"There they are," said Ivan.

I searched the view beneath us. Over to the right of the tent. Two red dots on the snowfield. Our sherpas.

"What are they doing here?" I asked.

Ivan said he called Tsering on the sat phone before we left Four. He was at Camp Two with Nawang. They'd climbed the entire Black Pyramid in the time it took us to walk partway down a big ski hill.

A sliver of warmth penetrated my frozen skull. Me on a rope team with three of the finest high-altitude climbers in the world. I'd get to feast on Raymond's cooking once more before my septic leg or rotting brain took me. It would be good to see the boys again, too. Companionship. Not being alone with Ivan anymore. I waved my dead left arm back and forth above my head.

I couldn't tell if they responded. Too far away.

"Should have told me they were coming," I said to Ivan's back.

Movement in the periphery of my vision. To my left two more dots of colour had appeared, but these ones were almost as high as we were, coming around the curve of the slope. They were descending rapidly. I saw purple and lime green. The two-tone suits were familiar.

"Italy's HAPs," said Ivan.

Stefano's companions at the traverse, the men who tried to save our lives, had worn purple and green. It made no sense. I thought they were gone, dead for sure. But here they were. I would have smiled but my face was frozen.

The Pakistani climbers were dropping fast.

"Are they glissading?" I asked Ivan.

A fancy word for sliding on your ass. You use your ice axe to steer, and to slow down when required. It's a quick way to get down a slope but not recommended in places with any risk of crevasses, avalanches, or lethal runouts. We encountered crevasses coming up to Four from Three. Hopefully the avalanche filled them.

The HAPs were not slowing down. They'd cross our path well below us.

"That doesn't look good," said Ivan. His tone was cheerful. He turned to look at me. He was grinning.

The red dots, our sherpas, had stopped moving. They must have seen the approaching HAPs. The glissaders streaked downhill towards them.

"Slow down!" I yelled. My voice was hoarse. The words died.

A rooster tail of snow was splashing up behind each of the two sliders. They were heading straight for the sherpas. Was it possible they hadn't seen the men beneath them, that they had no idea they were risking a collision? It was incredibly reckless. My stomach contorted itself in a knot of tension and fear.

The purple and green of the first HAP reached the red dot on our right. The colours entangled as they dropped from view down the Black Pyramid.

The second sherpa jumped out of the way of the second oncoming HAP. There was a flash of light, a reflection on metal. The glissader kept sliding, a red figure pulled behind it.

"Got him with the ice axe," said Ivan.

The second pair vanished over the edge.

CHAPTER THIRTY

AUGUST 5

IVAN WASN'T IVAN. The guide that led me to the top of K2 was gone.

He was whistling. He was outside the tent, whistling as he scooped snow into a pot to brew some water. Had it even been an hour since Tsering and Nawang were pulled to their deaths? The stress had finally gotten to him. The super-man was just human. Broken.

"You know, I've been thinking," said the guide's disembodied voice.

I couldn't see him. I was buried in my sleeping bag. When my eyes were open I was still at Camp Three. When I closed them, I saw my teammates sliding over the precipice.

"Like, where did those guys even come from?" he continued.

I had no idea. We'd lost them days ago when we came down the Bottleneck in the storm. They'd been without tents all that time. No one could live exposed on the upper slopes of K2 for that long. Maybe they found one of the Italian shelters that blew away in the storm? Oh, and here was a mystery to ponder: Why had they become suicidal murderers?

"The mountain does crazy things to some people," said Ivan, answering a question I never voiced.

I didn't want to be lying in my sleeping bag. I wanted to keep going. I was exhausted but the last thing I wanted to do was stop for the night. Ivan said it was too dangerous, though, to descend the Black Pyramid. The day was too warm. We needed to wait for the freeze, head out early the next morning.

The zipper opened. I looked up at the sound. Ivan poked his head in. I could see bone under the black rot of his missing nose. He smiled. His teeth looked terrible: milky, translucent even, and seated in gums that had turned blue. I looked away.

"Are you hungry? I'm starving," he said.

He knew we were out of food. We left everything on the Shoulder.

"Losing Tsering and Nawang was a waste of good food."

Did he really say that?

"What?" I spat. "What are you talking about?"

He sat beside me, the weight of his leg pressing against my thigh as he assumed a cross-legged position.

"They were bringing food up, among other things. So close to a good meal, then–," he snapped his fingers. "Really makes you think."

I was amazed. Horribly astounded.

"What exactly does it make you think, Ivan?"

His tone was conversational as he continued.

"Life, man, life. This place can snuff you out like an eighteen-wheeler flattens frogs on a road after the rain. Squish-squash, squish-squash," – his blackened head tick-tocked back and forth – "squish-squash, squish-squash. One second you're alive and the next you're being murdered with an ice axe, right? Or torpedoed by a tobogganer. What it makes you think, Phil – since you and me, we're thinking together now – is that you're going to be dead in the blink of an eye. You. And forever is a really long time to be alone and cold."

He leaned down to whisper the final words. His breath felt like spider legs on my skin. A shudder ran through my body.

"Why, you're pretty darn cold right now," he said. "Tea will warm you up. Almost ready."

I sat up when he moved. His back was to me as he poured water into a cup.

I could kill him. He was supposed to be dead. I could kill him with the knife I had strapped to my harness.

Something went wrong on top of the mountain. He wasn't supposed to be alive. He said good-bye – I said good-bye – and then we went to sleep and in the morning he was supposed to be gone except he wasn't.

We were both supposed to die up there.

He turned to me with the cup. His teeth looked normal. His nose was a crater – bone definitely visible – but he was still Ivan. Maybe I was just losing my shit.

The tea was good. I sipped the brew and Ivan sipped his. Quiet, thank god. I finished my cup and suggested we turn in for the night.

"I'm going to melt more snow for water but you get some rest," he said. "Big day tomorrow. We should make it down to One."

I couldn't sleep. I wanted to. Nothing was more appealing than unconsciousness. But I couldn't sleep with Ivan sitting beside me. I imagined him watching me. I felt his eyes on me. I must have fallen asleep for a second, though, because I woke up and he was whistling again.

I finally placed the song. I heard the lyrics in my head:

There's a dark and a troubled side of life;
There's a bright and a sunny side, too;
Tho' we meet with the darkness and strife,
The sunny side we also may view.

Of course I knew it. I used to have the "O Brother Where Art Thou?" soundtrack on CD.

Tho' the storm in its fury break today,
Crushing hopes that we cherished so dear,
Storm and cloud will in time pass away,
The sun again will shine bright and clear.

Ivan burst into song: "Keep on the sunny side, always on the sunny side. Keep on the sunny side of life!"

I was starving, freezing, hypoxic and stranded in a tent with a maniac. The sheer absurdity of the situation struck me as hilarious.

"It will help us every day, it will brighten all the way," I shouted into my down sleeping bag, "if we keep on the sunny side of life!"

I laughed. I laughed because life is terrifying and amazing, the universe used to be a tiny dot, my skull is full of slime, I don't know a damn thing about anything – and all of that could be okay if I just decided it was.

Ivan didn't laugh. His silence buried me. Corrupted night expanded to fill the tent. I coughed at the taste of stale grease in my throat. I wanted to run – I wanted to throw myself off the Black Pyramid – but could only muster the strength for six choked words.

"No more whistling. No more songs."

CHAPTER THIRTY-ONE

AUGUST 6

I WOKE IN the dark to a blast of cold air. Ivan had unzipped the tent.

"Follow me," he said.

He stepped outside. I remained in my bag. I heard the crunch of crampons as they bit into ice. He was walking, the sound fading quickly. My guide was leaving.

I was out of the sleeping bag a moment later. I hated what Ivan had become. But I needed him. I needed his knowledge to descend the Abruzzi. I even needed his company – his sick, rotting company – to keep me from total panic. The thought struck me that if the sound of his crampons passed beyond my hearing, I'd die.

I'd go insane. I'd leap to my death.

I couldn't let him get away.

As long as I was with him, there was still a chance. Maybe death wouldn't take me. There was no time to gather my things. I was already wearing my down suit and boots. I hadn't dared remove my footwear. With my left foot frozen, the boot would never have gone back on. I attached my crampons inside the tent, not caring that I was tearing the floor of the shelter to ribbons with the spikes. I was out the door of the tent with a bottle of water in one gloved hand and my ice axe in the other. I had my harness with carabiners and descender, and my headlamp, too, but nothing else.

He was gone. The night was clear and I couldn't see him anywhere. I clipped into the fixed rope that descended from the tent. I walked to the lip of the pyramid and peered down into the dark.

A faint ting of metal and a flicker of light at least a full pitch down.

"Ivan!" I shouted. I didn't hear a response. I clipped onto the fixed rope and started rapping down.

There was no food in my stomach, no fuel in my muscles. My body was eating itself to stay energized. I missed a foot placement and fell sideways, smashing my head into a protruding piece of ice. I could taste the impact in my mouth, a flavour like sucking on pennies.

My helmet. I'd left it behind. A stupid mistake. Maybe lethal. I wasn't going back, though.

176

My frozen leg was almost useless. I couldn't feel anything through that foot. I had to guess when the crampons were planted. I looked down between my legs. I could barely see my partner's headlamp.

"Damn you, Ivan," I said to myself.

An hour passed. Another hour. The lamp was always below me, always on the next pitch. I was slowing down. I'd been dropping forever and I was still not at the bottom. (Was I still sure there was a bottom?)

I couldn't feel either of my hands anymore. I had to watch them intently to make sure they did what I needed them to do.

A pause at the start of the next pitch. I needed water. I raised the bottle to my lips and discovered it was frozen solid. I was hauling a bottle of ice down the mountain. I placed it on a frozen rock beside my waist. It slid off the boulder and vanished. I looked between my feet for Ivan's lamp and tried to see if it suddenly changed, some indication he'd been hit. But the distant will-o-wisp held steady. I hadn't bombed my guide.

My headlamp quit just as I was about to start moving again. The darkness was complete, the black of a tight tunnel deep underground. I didn't have batteries. Wouldn't have mattered anyway. My frozen fingers were almost useless.

"Ivan!"

It came out as an inhuman croak. I thought of Varney's alien voice. Maybe he just needed a drink of water, like me.

The light from Ivan's headlamp was a dot. A period becoming a pinpoint. I needed to switch my descender to the new rope and start down the next pitch. We had to be close to the bottom. Ivan would wait for me at Camp Two, wouldn't he?

I couldn't see what I needed to do. I couldn't feel what I needed to do, either. It was absurd: I was holding the rope in my left hand and my right hand was trying to attach the device; it wasn't a complicated procedure. I'd be damned, though, if I could manage it.

There. Almost had it. Just needed to slide a piece of metal over.

Something hit me in the head. Right in the centre, on the top. The pain was instant and penetrating, like a skewer plunged through the crown of my skull. I gasped and sagged. My grip on the device loosened. I reached for the rope with my other hand.

The rope wasn't there.

I lost my balance. I was flailing with my good arm. I tried to clutch something, anything, tried to grab air and fly to safety.

I fell.

THIS IS IT.

Then movement stopped. My head struck something hard. An eruption, a flare of light in my cranium. I thought I'd smashed my brains – I'm done for – but no, Jesus, oh Jesus fuck: My leg! Lava-fire torment. A woodchipper of agony beyond imagining.

Everything was pain, every sense a shriek of tearing metal and agony. My leg, god my leg. It was unbearable.

I didn't know how far I'd fallen. Surely not far. What had I done to my left leg? I fell, then I hit. Ten metres, maybe less. I didn't dare move. I didn't know why I wasn't a thousand feet lower, splattered down the cliffside in a crimson smear. Just lucky.

It didn't feel like luck. My head, my leg – my back, too – the sensation was blinding. I could hardly breathe.

"Ivan!"

I screamed the word. Froth blasted out of my frozen lips. Again: "Eye-Vaann!"

I patted the ground beneath me with my right hand. Resting on something solid. Hard, cold rock. I crabbed my fingers across the surface and found a good grip, a perfect jug like a hold on a climbing wall. I couldn't sit up, though. I was afraid to move at all, afraid the pain would surge and I'd faint. What would I find if I mustered the courage to touch the storming locus of agony in my leg? Had a ragged, splintered end of a bone emerged from my thigh, burst through my down suit like a Ridley Scott alien?

I wished I had the last of Ivan's syringes. I needed drugs. Something. Anything.

"Ivan, you sonuvabitch! Get up here. I need you!"

He would come back. He'd get to the bottom of the pyramid and when I didn't join him, he'd come back up.

Unless he didn't.

He told me when he left camp. If he really wanted to leave me behind, truly abandon me, he would have snuck away without a word. This was supposed to be some kind of lesson. That had to be it. A messed-up graduation challenge.

If it *was* a test, though, I'd failed, and an "F" in this class apparently meant abandonment, because he still hadn't returned. Two minutes became fifteen became half an hour. The pain dulled a little. I tested my grip on the rock again and used my fading strength to pull myself into a seated position.

"Shii-ii-it!"

I had to yell. If I hadn't my head would have burst in an explosion of green goop like the Martians in Mars Attacks.

178

I didn't dare let go with my right grip. I needed to know the condition of my left leg but I couldn't see it in the dark and I'd lost all sensation in my left hand. Was I on a boulder? It felt like it. A flat surface a little more than a metre across. Nice place for a picnic.

I couldn't see anything when I looked down. Looking up was no better. Maybe I'd broken through to another dimension. Maybe I'd died and gone to the afterlife, a crappy heaven where my leg was busted, everything hurt and it was really freakin' cold.

I couldn't stay there. My head was exploding with pain. What hit me? It couldn't have been very big or I'd have been killed outright. I tried to bend the leg. Nausea flooded my abdomen and pressed on my lungs. I felt my grip on the wall weaken.

Hold on. Hold on. The pain receded. It took a few timeless seconds to fade into background misery.

I had nothing with me. No first aid supplies. I kept a roll of medical tape in my bag: tough, sticky fabric that could serve as a bandaid or tensor bandage, even patch a tent or mend a broken strap. If I had the tape I could do something. The tape was at Camp Three on the dark side of the moon.

I read *Touching the Void*. Joe Simpson broke his leg high on a mountain and survived. But I was not Joe Simpson. I didn't have his knowledge, I was ten thousand feet higher, and half my limbs were frozen. I'd just spent a week in and out of the death zone, including a bivouac above eight thousand metres.

Boo hoo. None of that really mattered. Altitudes and temperature, calories consumed and water lost. Willpower trumps them all. Joe Simpson lived because he wanted to. He believed he had something to live for. And I just didn't anymore.

The squeeze of tension in my chest abated just a little. The pain in my leg was vivid but it was only a sensation, not a threat.

I said the words quietly. A test.

"I want to die."

The words made sense. It was what I came to K2 to do. I'd been running from death: fighting it, fearing it; wishing for another month, just one more day; another memory, a last chance to see Karen. And that was fine. I was supposed to do those things. What I wasn't supposed to do, though, was wallow in fear and allow cowardice to take hold.

We all face a final test of courage. You can spend your whole life running away; duck down the alley to avoid the bully, pretend you didn't hear the insult to avoid confronting it. You can't hide from death, however. We all have to meet it. It will find us. So I yelled. I yelled at the mountain.

"I'm ready. You hear me? Let's go. Come on, let's find out!"

I was shouting at K2. I was shouting at my tumour. I was shouting at a god I wished I could believe in.

I was shouting at whatever made Ang a killer and whatever blew him off the mountaintop. Because Ang *was* a killer. He killed his best friend on top of K2. Ivan was dead. Someone else led me down the mountain.

Some*thing* else.

A light flared in front of my face. Blinding, crystal facets of white. I blinked but didn't raise a hand to block it. I wasn't even surprised.

The light moved from my face to my leg. No bones sticking out of the down suit. Didn't matter. Didn't change anything.

I squinted past the colour spots blooming in my vision. The light was coming from a headlamp worn by an upside-down man. He was clinging to the rock face just above me, his head less than a metre away from my face.

"Is that you, Ivan?" I asked.

"You know it's not," said Ivan's mouth with Varney's voice.

The light from the headlamp felt very cold. The heat of absolute zero. It was blinding if I stared directly into it. Comforting.

"I don't understand," I said. "Why put me through all of this?"

"You did it to yourself," said the light. "You needed to. I was just waiting for you to give up."

Is that what this was? Had I surrendered? It didn't feel like surrender. More like acceptance.

I was glad he'd come back for me. I didn't want Varney to leave.

"You never have to be alone again," he said.

The light moved closer, filled my whole field of vision. I smelled the rot. I could hear the snick of needle-scissor teeth as Varney leaned towards the left side of my head. He whispered in my ear.

"Don't feel bad," he said. "You made it to the top all on your own. So what if I had to help your frozen legs on the way back down?"

My hand released its grip on the rock face. Not my choice. I was no longer in control. My body rose smoothly to its feet. I felt nothing in my legs. I bent over like I was going to touch my toes. Then I leaned even further. For a second I thought I was going to swan-dive into the abyss, but my hands found holds on the rocks beneath me.

I started clambering down the cliff head-first.

Varney's headlamp lit a narrow swath of the route I was descending. Broken, frozen rock, shadows and bottomless black. The headlamp moved. It was beside me, then it sped up, dropping from point to point, like a monkey descending a tree.

My body moved faster. My breathing continued steadily, unaffected by the exertions of my flesh, unaffected by fear. I wasn't even sure I *was* scared.

I'd always thought of fear as a mental state, but maybe it's not. Maybe fear is physical. Can a brain really panic in a calm body? I was spidering my way down a vertical wall in pursuit of two equally wondrous and terrible possibilities: Varney was real or I was utterly delusional. Both were terrifying options. Yet the moment in which I existed was devoid of the chemical markers – the meat biology – of terror. I felt calm.

The light stopped below me. I caught up after another minute of upside-down scrambling.

"A new day begins," Varney said. He reached up a backwards hand and turned off his headlamp. I was plunged into pitch black, but only for a moment. Darkness was giving way to daylight. There was a faint purple on the horizon and I could see my companion. Varney was wearing Ivan's horribly disfigured face but I looked past it. I saw what he was, or, more accurately, what he wasn't.

Not human. Not even flesh.

Something else. Something true. A glimpse – the tiniest, scorching impression – of real power and real weight, next to which the apparent solidity of the material world was just dust and shallows.

He stepped towards me. Would I have backed up if I'd been in control of my body? Would I have fallen on my face? Would I have embraced his ankles, grateful to burn in his proximity?

He placed his hands on my shoulders. I looked into the ruined face.

"You're a lucky man," Varney said. "I have a gift for you. A priceless treasure. But first you should drink tea."

I followed him downhill. I had no choice in the matter. My legs moved, my diaphragm inhaled and exhaled, my brain watched. I wasn't lying to myself, though: I would have chosen to follow.

Our tents at Camp Two still stood. Varney produced a stove from inside the shelter I shared with Ivan on the way up. I squatted down and shuffled into the tent. I recognized the temperature of the atmosphere around me – my skin felt the icy air – but it didn't penetrate. If anything, I was starting to feel a little warm, even hot. I unzipped my down suit. I seemed to have regained use of my limbs, although that was suspicious. I knew I had extensive frostbite, but my arms and hands, even my legs and feet, felt good.

"Tea should be ready in a moment," Varney said. "You want to phone Karen?"

"I thought we had to save the battery?"

I realized how nonsensical my words were as they spilled out of my mouth. He handed me the sat phone. I clambered out into the early morning light and waited for a signal. I looked into the tent. From behind, it could have been Ivan hunched over the little burner.

I punched in my ex-wife's cell number. The phone connected.

"Hello?"

Her voice. I smiled.

"It's me," I said.

"Oh thank God."

"Kind of," I said.

She asked where I was. I told her. Then she surprised me.

"I'm at Camp One," she said. "I'm just below you."

My ears were broken, apparently. I asked her to repeat what she'd said.

"I'm at Camp One. Your camp manager Raymond is here with me. He wouldn't take me any higher. I'm here, Phil. You asked me to meet you and I did. I'm going to take you home."

I was stunned. I felt happy, very happy. And also very confused: I asked you to meet me? It was a little irritating. Sort of like having a popcorn kernel stuck between your teeth when you find out you've won the lottery. You're overjoyed about the money, definitely, but goddamn if that popcorn isn't making you just a little bit crazy.

All I managed to say was, "Home?"

She told me to come down to One. She told me I could make it, then asked if I really could.

"I think so," I said. "I got to the top, Karen. I made it to the top. But Ang is dead. And Ivan is – Ivan, he –"

"You're going to tell me in person," she said. "You come right down as soon as you can. One night at Camp Two, no more, and then you start down no matter what."

I hung up. I forgot to tell her I loved her. It didn't matter. She knew.

"How's the wife?" Varney asked.

He was standing in front of me, holding out a cup of tea. Steam rose from the titanium mug.

"She's here," I answered. "She's on K2, just below us, at Camp One."

His mouth formed a shocked 'O'. It was no longer Ivan's face; needle teeth like glass syringes, greasy wetness smeared around the orifice.

"She is? Well, what a wonderful surprise," he said.

I didn't know if he was even speaking. Maybe the words were just forming in my head. Varney pushed the mug into my good hand.

"Take this already," he said. "You've made me wait long enough. You're like a hobbled granny on Christmas morning, all the kids waiting for her to shuffle to the tree so they can finally start opening their presents. It's time to rip the wrapping off this gift."

My hand raised the cup to my mouth and I drank. The sensation of being a passenger in my own body returned.

"You're going to die really soon," he said. "You'd be dead already if it weren't for me."

"You tried to kill me on the summit," I said.

"I did not try to kill you. I was having fun. Your horror was electrifying. But then Ang got stubborn and cut the game short. He defied me, so I threw him off my mountain.

"Look, I will grant that my motives have not been entirely altruistic," he continued. "Sticking it to Ivan and Ang was a delight only exceeded by your suffering. Will Phil make it to the top or won't he? Will he just completely lose his shit and kill himself? Getting to participate in your journey has been a true joy. The highlight of my century. The hour's late, though. We only have one game left to play, and this one has the highest stakes. If you win this one, you win it all. *We* win it all.

"I know this will be hard for you to grasp, Phil, but you haven't seen a fraction of what I can do. This stuff, this rock and flesh and cold and heat, is so foul, so crude. In this polluted realm, I'm a master sculptor reduced to wielding a sledgehammer. You *have* helped me. My power has grown. Together, the hammer has become a wrecking ball, and I'm grateful for that. What you haven't seen, though – what you can't see yet – is how much more we can become."

I didn't understand. He'd lost me. And Karen was at Camp One. Why was Karen at Camp One?

"You look confused. Are you confused?" he said. His two bulging eyes were drifting towards each other. "What I'm saying is that your Plato was right. Humans live in a cave. But you don't have to, Phil, not anymore. All you have to do is join me. I can lead you out of the darkness. Choose me. Become mine. Then I can show you."

The eyes were merging, like two glops of rancid pudding pushing into each other.

"You'll live forever. No, really, you and Karen can live forever. I'm offering to cut you loose from this pathetic existence. What I'm offering," he leaned forward as I stared into his cyclops eye with two pupils, "is to save you from the even more pathetic non-existence waiting for you when that tumour finally ends your sad run.

"You've seen death, Phil. I've shown it to you. It smells, it's ugly and it's permanent; everything you are, everything you care about, reduced to a wet stain."

She said I asked her to come. When did I do that?

"It was me," said Varney. "You were sleeping and I invited her. Look, it doesn't matter. Are you even listening to me? You've got a decision to make: frozen steak in the glacier or join me forever."

"What?"

"Eternity, Phil, eternity with Karen! That's what's at stake here. I can't really describe it to you, either. I could try but honestly there's no point – like trying to explain spaceflight to a snail."

Could this just be my brain, my fucked up, diseased brain? I mean, it had to be, right?

"No, it's not," he countered. "It's a wonderful surprise, that's what it is. I couldn't let you use the sat phone at Camp Four because I had to give her time to get here. I didn't even know she *was* here, not until I felt her starting uphill from Advanced Base Camp."

We would descend to Camp One in the early hours of the morning. I was going to see Karen again in less than a day.

"We're not waiting," Varney said. "I'm walking those legs of yours down this mountain with or without your permission."

I should have been overjoyed. I *was* overjoyed. I was also shattered. My mind felt fried.

"I can't handle this. I think I'm going insane," I muttered.

"Bullshit," he answered. "You just need a little pick me up."

Ivan's pack lay on the ground. Varney shoved a claw in the bag and came out with a syringe. I didn't feel the jab of the needle in my frozen thigh but the effect of the drug was instant.

"Oh wow. That's incredible," I blurted. Power surged through my dying limbs. Euphoria flooded my brain.

"Nothing compared to what's waiting for you," he said.

I asked Varney if we needed to pack up. The being's round mouth morphed into a horizontal oval. His version of a smile.

"You're leaving it, Phil. You're leaving all of it," he said.

Ivan's body turned and walked away from me. My legs started after him. He didn't bother clipping in to the fixed rope, and he didn't secure me either. Not even a short-rope connected us.

"What's the worst that can happen?" he said over his shoulder. "You die?"

I rode along in my meat chariot. My feet and hands weren't mine to control. My brain fast-percolated with pharmaceuticals.

"Why Karen?" I asked.

"Why not?" Varney answered. "We're teammates, you and me. Only one thing could be better than life eternal and that's life eternal with the woman you love."

I was confused.

"Are we going to Heaven?"

We were jumping down the mountain, hopping from rock to boulder.

"I don't use that word," he said. "I've never met God or an angel, and I've never seen a lake of fire or a red guy with a pitchfork either. Those notions are so small, aren't they? Ideas born of ignorance. Virgins in volcanoes."

He leapt across a five-metre crevasse. I followed and cleared the gap with a body-length to spare. I felt weightless. Mighty.

"How can you do this?" I said. "What *are* you?"

"I am hunger and thirst," he answered. "A devouring fire brought to this place by a sorcerer."

A sorcerer?

"Like Gandalf the wizard?" I said.

I felt the ground beneath my feet rumble as Varney chuckled.

"A climber, one of the first to come here, with knowledge he never should have had."

Did Varney put the name in my mind or did I miss my calling as a Jeopardy contestant?

"Crowley. You're talking about Aleister Crowley," I said. "The story was true."

"If only he'd performed the ritual a little further down the mountain," said Varney, "Ang and Ivan wouldn't have avalanched out of my reach the first time."

We arrived at the top of the chimney. Ivan's body didn't slow. It dropped into the chute without using any of the ropes choking the top entrance. My body followed. My hands and feet pushed against the encroaching, ice-coated walls, facing out the whole way down. It felt like descending from the clouds in a glass elevator.

He waited for me at the bottom.

"I'll get you to Camp One, Phil," Varney said. "I've been helping your body ever since the bivouac. But here's the critical point: I can't do the last part for you. You have to choose. You have to find your courage and save yourself. Save yourself and save Karen."

Save Karen. Yes, that made sense. I had to do that.

"The question is, do you have what it takes?" he said. "Can you do the impossible to win the unimaginable?"

Varney turned and started downhill again. He was speeding up. Sprinting. I was never more than a few paces behind.

I didn't know how fast we were moving. I felt like I was part of the mountain. I was an avalanche and we were going to bury Karen and Raymond when we reached them. For some reason that didn't disturb me. It felt exhilarating. The pleasure a polar bear feels when its teeth grip a seal.

I could see the outcrop of rock that concealed Camp One. I laughed, giddy with excitement. The Ivan shell threw back its head and howled, an alien horn-blast echoing across the mountainside.

We covered the intervening slope in less than a minute. I leapt to the top of the exposed granite that shielded the tiny campsite. Our two orange tents were perched on the narrow ledge below. Varney alighted beside me.

"You must harden your heart for a brief moment," he said. "A flicker of cruelty and then you can both join me."

"I don't understand," I said.

That wasn't entirely true. I had some sense what was required. My possessed hands flexed and relaxed, flexed and relaxed. My body (was it still mine?) was thirsty.

The vestibule of a tent bulged and the nylon fabric deposited a slight figure in a multicoloured ski jacket onto the narrow strip of level ground beneath me. A second, larger person emerged from the shelter. The first – it had to be Karen – turned and offered a helping hand to her companion. Her back was to me when I dropped twenty feet to the ground and landed soundlessly on my frozen leg.

"Karen," I said.

It *was* her. Impossible but true. She'd had a haircut. A short, pixie style. It suited her. She looked beautiful. An oxygen bottle was slung over her back. Thin, clear hoses looped over her ears and across her full cheeks to meet at her nose.

Karen stretched out her arms. I walked to her, reached over her shoulders and pulled her close. Raymond was on his feet. A rare smile opened on his face. The next second it dropped.

He was looking past me. I didn't need to turn. I knew who had dropped to the ledge behind me – knew *what* was standing there. Cold and heat roared off the figure of Varney – my new guide – and passed through my body like a hurricane of lethal radiation.

"Thank you for bringing him back to me, Ivan," Karen said to Varney.

She had no sense of the danger. How could she not feel it, Moby Dick rising from the deep beneath her? I could tell by the way she adjusted the angle of her head that she could see over my shoulder. She was looking right at It. What was she seeing? Just a weary guide returned from a tough expedition?

I locked eyes with Raymond. He wasn't *seeing*, not yet – his expression was just suspicious, not horrified – but something was sounding an alarm inside him. Some primitive instinct left over from when we were rodents flashed deep in his brain stem, a warning from an epoch when survival depended on being too small to warrant interest from the giant dragons that inhabited the world.

I liked Raymond. I wanted to tell him he was too late.

Karen froze, a statue in my arms. A great rush of air blasted my back. I'd have fallen over if Varney hadn't been in control of my body. A tree trunk of pale flesh appeared over my head, casting a long shadow that stretched over the tents.

It arched forward, beyond me, past Karen. The end of the monstrous appendage – I could see slipping, flicking tendrils – dropped on Raymond like a piano, enveloped his head and his upper body, inhaling him from the waist up.

Terror and repulsion have a sound. They slither and suck. Then they roar like a chainsaw spearing a rotten pumpkin.

The thick column of pale tissue yanked back even more swiftly than it struck, leaving some of the head porter behind: Raymond from the waist down only, legs still standing, a vivisection line passing cleanly through his Gore-Tex jacket and guts.

"Now, Phil," said the terrible voice. "It's time."

My hands squeezed Karen's shoulders. She hadn't seen Raymond, her stare fixed over my shoulder. Her eyes were wild and filled with tears, and her mouth quivered. I didn't want to imagine what Varney looked like now, what she was seeing. I was focused on her, the miracle of her face, the only person I'd ever loved.

"B-B-Bobby said I sh-sh-shouldn't come," she stammered.

Clean rage jetted through my head, torched love, reduced sentiment and empathy to ash. Was it my anger or was it Varney's? Was there still a difference?

"Bobby was wrong," we said. "Bobby is nothing. He could never give you this."

My frozen hands released her shoulders and grabbed her face. She blinked. When her eyes opened again she was staring at me. She saw me.

She finally saw what I was becoming.

My palms pressed into her cheeks. Searing heat flowed out of her, through my gloves, into my brittle claws. She gasped. Her eyes started to roll back. Karen choked out a single word. "– D-don't –"

My eyes closed.

CHAPTER THIRTY-TWO

AUGUST 6

A SENSATION LIKE ice pellets stinging my face, stabbing my eyelids. A deep vibration passed up through my legs and into my chest, demanding unison with my heartbeat. Then there was silence and calm. I opened my eyes.

I stood on the summit of a mountain. The symmetrical snow pyramid dropped away from my feet steeply to the shores of a roiling cloud-sea the colour of ink. The storm waves flowed in expanding circles around my perch.

The peak was at the centre of a swirling vortex of clouds stretching to an opaque grey horizon.

I was warm. A nostalgic summer heat. I looked up at the sun and found that it was only a bird's flight above. A brown-orange ball almost as big as the island on which I stood hovered low in the sky over me. Nuclear fire boiled on its surface, blossomed like murderous flowers and sank like perishing souls.

"Phil Truss!"

The voice was Varney's, but only in the sense that I could feel it was him and there was no other it could be. The choked, artificial timbre was gone, replaced with a quality I could barely begin to describe. The proto-conscious noise a bee hears in its head when it stabs with its stinger, killing itself for the power to inflict pain. The scream of a decaying boson amplified to fill a Dyson sphere. Something on the edge of comprehension.

The sound waves had substance, though, a booming projection from the inferno suspended overhead. I hunched my shoulders to bear their weight.

"All that came before is gone," said the sun. "All that can be is in your grasp."

I looked down at my hands. Black fingers stretched too long out of the worn wool cuffs of a tweed climbing blazer. I looked down at my feet. They were encased in hob-nailed leather boots.

Why am I here?

"You are here to win the future for you and your bride," Varney roared. "You stand at the beginning of new life, witness to the moment that precedes ignition. Now turn around, Phil. Have courage and become."

I turned. Karen was standing behind me, facing me, dressed in her climbing clothes.

189

My beautiful wife. Her eyes were open and she was smiling. I started to smile. Then I realized she was immobile, her eyes fixed, her expression frozen.

"Karen? Baby?" I started to reach for her with one of my desiccated claws but stopped when I realized the fingers were gripping the handle of my climbing knife.

I closed my eyes. I could feel myself swaying, trying to find balance. I felt confused. The clarity that had possessed me as I'd run down the mountain had evaporated.

The thought was fully formed when it appeared in my mind: Mighty Varney couldn't allow Karen to be real in this moment. This was the best he could do. If Karen was allowed a voice, she'd be screaming, her face contorted in horror. And if Varney tried to animate her, I would see the falsehood, know the lie – a lewd replica of my ex-wife, with extra teeth and backwards hands.

A great burden sloughed off my shoulders, like a lead shroud tearing under its own weight.

I opened my eyes again. "None of this is real," I said.

How long had his poison been corrupting my mind? Did it start after the summit, at Camp Four? No, it was earlier than that. The accident at the traverse, maybe before. My body was dying, that had been true for months, but Varney had been killing my soul.

A great blast of air greeted my dismissal. I staggered, barely caught my balance.

"You are wrong, Phil. Wrong like Ptolemy was when he described the movement of the planets," the voice boomed. "This is more real than the puppet theatre you've performed in since the day your insect existence began."

He was a monster inviting me to become a monster.

"How many people have you killed?" I said. I looked up at the glowing orb. It filled my field of vision. I could detect no change in its chaos when it replied.

"How many raindrops have touched your face?" said Varney. "Many thousands. A deluge. The flood slowed when I became trapped on this mountain, but your presence has been liberating. We've achieved so much already! So rest your conscience; the ethical dilemmas of caterpillars don't concern you anymore. Humans are our prey and it's right that we feed. Now complete your metamorphosis and penetrate Karen with your knife."

My eyes flickered down to the blade. It was no longer steel; a razor-shard of black stone that bit into my mummified fingers, ripped the parchment skin.

I can't do this.

"I won't," I said aloud.

The ever-shifting sun didn't change its non-pattern but I could see a great ripple streak through the black cloud sea, drive greasy billows up the snow before subsiding.

"You're a good germ, Phil, a kindly bug," said Varney.

I'm not. I'm self-absorbed and greedy, fearful and weak.

"Of course," he said, "but only in the way most decent humans are. The final steps require honest cruelty and that's difficult for most people. Difficult for you. And that's why I invited Karen: to make this easier."

I looked at her face, realizing as I did so that I'd been avoiding doing so. What if she was here and awake? What if every word he said was heard by her? What if she could hear my thoughts?

"You will stab the woman you love because I'm giving you an easy choice. Do as I demand and she can join you with me. I am a generous master. I will feed on you, and you will taste of my power.

"Understand what I offer, Phil," he continued. "This will never end. Never. Stars will exhaust themselves, physical laws will bend and devolve into entropy, and there will still be you and Karen. You will have her for all time. Wouldn't she want that?"

The answer came immediately to mind. No.

I wasn't sure that *I* wanted it. An inconceivable destiny paid for with infinite victims. Eternal life inflicting death eternally.

But...I would have Karen.

But Varney would have us. My mind balked at what it would mean to be his possessions. If I was uncertain for myself, I had no doubt Karen would reject the offer. I would be obliterating the life of the woman I loved and spending an eternity with her despising me for it.

...but I would have Karen...

Enough thinking. I tried to let go of the knife. My fingers were locked in place around the stone.

"I cannot force your hand, Phil," said the sun. "But I can punish your failure to act."

"Refuse my offer and I will turn all of my attention to the utter demolition of you and the woman you love. Your torment will fuel my creativity and strengthen my cruelty. I will defile Karen in ways you cannot imagine, reduce her to a putrid, moldering husk. I will slow your tumour's growth for years and she will be your corrupted companion the whole time: a shattered reminder of your cowardly refusal to save her.

"You will hate yourself, certainly, but you will *despise* her. You'll beg for permission to wrap your hands around her throat – not to end her misery, but to end your own."

As he spoke, Karen transformed. Her eyes yellowed, turned purple, then burst. Teeth sprouted behind her teeth, row after row, crowding and pushing until her mouth started to expand. Her stretched lips thinned until they were a desiccated line framing an ivory stockade of bristling fangs. Above the teeth, her skin shrank and blackened. Something small, ebony and shiny squirmed in each of her vacant eye sockets.

She raised her arms; no longer hand, skin and elbow, but hinged, mantid hooks.

My reaction was guided by fear. I punched my hand forward into her abdomen, felt only the slightest resistance as the point of the stone blade pushed into flesh and invaded her body. She fell onto her back. The monstrosity was gone. Karen had returned, but Karen when we first met. She looked twenty again. Her eyes were closed. A small smile raised the corner of her lips. The knife stuck out of her clothing just below where her navel would be.

What did I do?

"Karen, oh god, I-I didn't want... I don't –" I started.

Whatever words I would have said next were atomized by a bellow from above.

"The first cut!" the voice roared.

I looked up at the sun and realized the burning I felt on my head was cold, not heat. A pitiless, absolute zero implacable in its savagery.

"Please. *Please*," I pleaded. "It has to be enough. I've done what you asked."

"Do you think eternity is sold so cheaply?" it continued. "The next strike will demand real intention. We need her eggs, Phil. You must cut them from her body..."

No. No, no, NO. I doubled over as my stomach spasmed and squeezed.

"...cut them from her body – and eat them! Only when they have germinated in the dirt of your viscera can the two of you be excreted into new life. Blood and filth are the currency and the price must be paid."

It would never end. Varney's appetite was bottomless.

I screamed. I raised my fists at the sun, then pounded them down on top of my head, hoping pain would provide even a second of distraction from the sickness and despair. I punched myself in the face, hammered my fist into my mouth, then dropped to my knees, every muscle flexed in the hope I could make myself explode. And when my strength ebbed, Varney's voice was still there.

"Complete your task," he said. "The ritual has begun and cannot be delayed. I demand action."

I felt a CRACK beneath my knees and feet. The sound reached my ears a moment later. I'd heard it often enough to recognize it immediately: an avalanche breaking free. I looked down the slope, scanning every direction, but the snow wasn't moving. The clouds, though – the violence of their movement against the mountain had increased.

"Phil."

It was Varney. His small voice. He was standing beside me. I wanted to strike him, attack, sink my teeth into one of his bulging eyes. But fatigue sapped my limbs. I felt like I was on top of K2 again.

He rested his backwards hand on my shoulder.

"Death is here, Phil," he said. "It's coming right now. I told you this would be difficult. I said you would need to do the impossible to attain the unimaginable. Those were my words."

I remembered. I remembered strength coursing through my blood, my body animated by Varney, by a power he said came from me.

"Here it comes, Phil," said the figure.

A wave of cold air rose up the slope and buffeted me. The black shores of the cloud-sea folded on themselves and split as a wall of snow emerged in a circle around the base of the cone. The snow was avalanching uphill, a wall of destruction that grew as it raced towards the summit.

"You have to do it now, Phil. Now! Cut her open. Tear her open and pull the seeds from her flesh. Flesh is muck and bile. Life has always come from such ugly beginnings."

The ground beneath my feet was bucking and shaking. It was hard to stand. Varney remained planted, though, and so did Karen sleeping on the summit. The tumbling ice and snow had surged more than halfway up the slope.

"Eternity with Karen or a stygian nightmare on K2. Is there really a choice?" he said.

A second blast of air pushed by the oncoming avalanche. Ice pellets and vapour drenched my wool clothes. The hurricane force of the wind momentarily took away my breath. When I could speak again, it was to think aloud.

"There has to be another way..." I began.

"There is no other way," Varney interrupted. "Doom is upon you."

The towering headwall of the avalanche was close enough that its top was almost level with where I stood. Mere seconds remained and panic threatened to paralyze me.

Two impossible, unacceptable choices. There had to be another option. The thunder of the avalanche was deafening.

I shouted the words as quickly as the inspiration came to me.

"You can have me forever, but not Karen. I don't want her with us."

Varney smiled. "Agreed," he said.

The avalanche towered above, reducing the sun to a vanishing orange disk at the top of a deep ice hole. Varney stepped backwards into the maelstrom. It swallowed him and Karen.

It swallowed me.

CHAPTER THIRTY-THREE

AUGUST 6

I PULLED MY hands off Karen's face. Her amazing face. My hands left red circles the size of an orange on each cheek, a brilliant contrast to her grey skin.

She collapsed to the ground. Pain levelled me less than a second later. I dropped to the snow from the agony of my frozen hands and feet, my broken leg and my wasted face and skin. My eyes were almost snow-blind – a blessing, I guess, because I could only see the outline of Ivan's form when I forced myself to look up at Varney.

"Your discomfort is temporary," he said. "Just a little reminder of what you are without me."

He stepped forward, a great shadow blocking out a beautiful, sunny day on K2. We really did have exceptional weather.

"The ritual isn't complete, Phil. Not quite. Protocols must be observed."

I didn't understand. And then I did.

The black tendrils that had invaded my vision in the death zone returned as live tentacles, flicked across my blurred sight, as Varney told me to draw my climbing knife.

"But you agreed," I pleaded.

"And I stand by our agreement. She will not join us. But blood must be spilled. Don't worry, I will be merciful. I'd love to watch you eat her face but I will sacrifice my own enjoyment this one time just to ease your transition. A single mouthful of her stuttering heart should fulfill the criteria."

"God. No. I told you I wouldn't. I can't. My hands are dead."

Varney smiled.

"In this place I can help," he said.

Power surged through my limbs, radiating from my belly. I sprang to my feet. Warmth cocooned my skull and seeped into my brain. I felt the change, struggled against it, but then I remembered why I'd been so excited about seeing Karen and sinking my teeth into her. My only regret – and it was a small thing, really – was that it was too late for her to come with me.

No matter. There would be so many others.

I reached up and grabbed the handle of my knife where it was velcroed in its sheath to my backpack strap. My grip was strong, no vestiges of mortal weakness, and my legs felt rooted to the mountain as I stepped over her prone body.

Did I really even need the knife? I could just start *ripping*.

A human shout. A war cry.

"Yaaah! Yaaah! Hawaaa!"

A shoulder smashed into my spine between my shoulders, sent me sprawling on top of Karen. Then a sound like a cleaver passing through meat into a wooden chopping block.

CHUN.

Weakness and pain dropped through me, filled me, like a giant bucket of cold water dumped over my back.

CHUN, CHUN…

The sound was repeated a dozen times. Fleshy and solid. Were the blows striking *me*? I couldn't tell. I was in agony, but it didn't feel like the agony of being chopped into pieces.

Quiet followed, broken only by the gasps of a person who'd exerted himself at altitude. One second passed. Five seconds. The crunch of crampons.

"Phil. Phil, it's me!" said an accented voice.

A face moved closer. I tried to pull away but only managed to roll off of Karen onto my back. My body was dying. I recognized Asian features, a sherpa.

"Dawa," I said. "I thought…didn't you fly out? You were supposed to fly out."

He smiled. Still smiling.

"I didn't want to go. Raymond said I could stay at Base Camp. He let me come up this one time in case you needed help. Oh Phil, Raymond is dead."

"I know," I said. "Dawa, where is Ivan? What did you do to him?"

Dawa frowned like the question made no sense.

"Ivan is not here. You know where Ivan is?"

"The thing, the creature, what did you do?" I asked.

His eyes flashed: "I killed it with my axe. My puja protects me. The mountain gods bless us."

I turned my head until I could see what was left of Ivan's body. Through my damaged eyes I saw a haze of blood-smeared clothing and haphazardly-chopped meat.

Fuck you, Varney.

Relief drew a sob from my chest. Everything hurt. My skin ached. There was no inch of my body that wasn't sore, and many places where the pain was sharp and insistent.

What I had almost done...what I had wanted to do...?

I couldn't think about it, wouldn't let myself.

"I will check on Karen," said Dawa.

Yes, do that. I don't matter. Take her from this place.

Dawa's voice spoke softly. There was no response. Tears leaked from my eyes.

"She's not answering," he said to me.

"Is she still breathing?" I asked.

They were the longest seconds of my life.

"She is breathing, yes."

"Then keep talking to her," I said.

It felt like a Herculean effort just turning my head. My whole body was poisoned with sepsis. Varney was the only thing that had kept me mobile. I managed to roll to my side. I was only a foot from Karen's face.

"I'm here, Karen," I said. "Karen, you gotta wake up."

There's no time. Varney is coming.

"Wake up, Honey," I said.

A soft sigh escaped her mouth.

"Bobby," she said quietly.

It hurt but I said yes.

Karen's eyes opened. For a moment she didn't understand. Then memory crushed her calm. She threw out her hand, hitting me in the face.

"No, no!" she said.

"It's me," I replied. "Look at me. I'm back. I won't hurt you, Karen. I'd never hurt you."

She raised herself up on one arm. Dawa had a hand on her bicep, steadying her. There was no place at Camp One that wasn't precarious. One wrong step and you'd be gone.

"Your face – you weren't you," she said. "And then the thing –"

She looked past me at Ivan's remains.

"Karen, we have to go," I said.

She looked behind her, in the direction of the tent.

"Where's Raymond?" she asked.

I looked for the remains of the head porter but didn't see them. They must have slid off the campsite. I hoped they weren't lodged in a rock where Karen would pass them.

"Dawa will tell you about it on the way down," I said. "Now get up and start moving."

She looked around uncertainly, like she expected another nasty surprise. Dawa maintained his grip on her arm as she stood. The sherpa already had a short-rope rigged. He clipped it onto Karen's harness. Then he started towards me. I raised my right hand.

"No, you have to go. Now," I said. I'd managed to sit up without revealing the agony the movement caused me. "I'm right behind you guys."

Karen took a step in my direction.

"We go down together," she said. "I'm not leaving without you."

I forced a smile. I hoped it looked natural.

"I'll be right behind you. I've been over these pitches a dozen times. I just want to pack up some gear and get rid of that," I threw a thumb over my shoulder in the direction of Ivan's remains.

"You're hurt," she said.

"I'm fine, and I'll get down quicker rappelling on my own than I would roping up with a newbie like you."

Dawa was still looking at me as she turned away. He wasn't smiling. He moved his head, just a subtle tilt in the direction of descent. I shook my head once.

"Move fast," I said to the sherpa, "and keep going until you reach Base Camp. Don't stop, not even for a minute – not until you're past ABC."

He nodded and gave me a thumbs up.

"And Dawa," I said, "don't ever come back to this place. Not ever. It took Ivan and Ang. Now it will want you."

Karen was looking at me again, the wind stiff enough to create ripples in her short hair.

"You're coming right now, yes?" she said.

How stupid I'd been. A whole living, breathing life I could have had with her. I smiled.

"I might even pass you."

My ex-wife started picking her way down the steep ice slope. Dawa was three metres behind her, one hand holding the short rope that tethered them together and the other wielding his lethal ice axe.

I love you, Karen.

My trip wasn't easy. One arm was useless and the other wasn't much better. My legs were dead. I took grim pleasure in the challenge, though, dragging myself as quickly as I could along the steep snow, while still being careful not to slide prematurely. I needed to get far enough that there was no chance I'd hit Dawa and Karen, or be seen by them.

I had to reach my destination before Varney returned. If I succeeded it might help Karen and Dawa. At least give them a chance.

I wanted to rest. Falling asleep would have been nice. I didn't dare. I wanted to leave as little as possible for him to use.

The pain faded. I could still feel it – every surface and every cavity – but it was distant. Real but inconsequential. I completed the traverse of the slope a foot at a time. I slid along the snow, one good hand my only means of locomotion. It took twenty minutes to reach my destination: a perilously steep ice slope thirty metres from the tents. It looked nearly vertical peering down. I couldn't see the drop-off but remembered it was there.

The wind felt warm. I knew it wasn't but that's how it felt. Through my clouded eyes I saw blue sky. A nice day to be on the mountain.

I heard the crunch of crampons on snow. I looked back in the direction of Camp One. Raymond's legs, attached at the pelvis, strode purposefully across the ice towards me.

You're too late, Varney. Whatever strength you get from me, I'm taking it away.

I would have laughed but I didn't have the energy. I let go instead. There was the briefest pause – Raymond's legs broke into a run – and then I was away, flying downhill.

I was a roller coaster, a rocketship.

A mountain.

A speck.

NOTES AND ACKNOWLEDGMENTS

Hello! This is Eric Sparling and I'm the author of *Peak*. Thank you so much for reading my book. Your time is valuable and I appreciate you spending some of it with me.

I am not a mountaineer. I've hiked up small peaks and I've had the good fortune to spend a bit of time roped-up on glaciers. Guides have taught me but I am not a stellar student. This book contains errors about the craft, and those errors are my fault entirely (one guide specifically told me he'd never short-rope someone who was also on a fixed line, but I've chosen to ignore his advice). I have also taken some liberties with the geography of K2. Much of the history I've relayed is true, and there really is a House's Chimney and a Bottleneck. Aleister Crowley really did climb on the mountain. But none of the adventurers whose accounts I've read mention an icefall at the start of the Abruzzi route, and pictures of the summit indicate it's not really spacious enough for the action sequence I've set there.

K2 is a spectacular bogeyman. I fear mountains and I'm drawn to them. Mountains are beautiful but my favourite landscapes are tamer, an idyllic mix of steep hills and rock outcrops, with groves of green trees breaking up green fields. When I get in high places, when I stand on a cliff or skirt the edge of a yawning crevasse, I think about death and courage. I think about how close I am to the end of my existence. I think about leaping into the void. I try to find the strength not to cower or flee. I value that struggle. It feels important.

Real people have died on K2. A lot of people. A grisly, supernatural story set on that notorious mountain runs the risk of being perceived as insensitive. The truth is this novel is a love letter to K2 as much as anything. I don't think climbing K2 is foolish and I don't think dying in the death zone is a wasted life—not if someone has entered that realm for the right reasons. And someone setting foot on K2 will almost always be there for the right reasons. By the time they climb its deadly and technical slopes, they are seasoned. They've probably lost friends in the mountains. Many have made sacrifices and difficult life choices, and asked loved ones to do the same. They know they could be leaving the mountain in a bag, or never leaving at all. But still they come to test themselves, or maybe to discover...

How *much* grinding exhaustion? How much thirst and hunger? How much beauty and transcendence? How much fear and loss?

How much *meaning*?

...or so I presume. The only times I've been above about 10,000 feet I've been in an airplane. I have been tired and scared in the mountains, however, and when I think about adding another 18,000 feet to my altitude, and weeks to my effort, and pounds to my pack—not to mention lethal rockfall, hurricane winds, and frostbite—well, I guess I end up writing a book like *Peak*.

So, a thank you first to the guides and teammates who've shared their adventures and knowledge with me. A debt of gratitude is owed, also, to the people who taught me how to write or fostered my efforts: instructors and editors, employers and colleagues, family and friends. I appreciate the time Tony and Alyson Fromm, Geoff Cruttwell, and Meghan Rose Allen have spent reading early drafts of this book and/or others. I also want to acknowledge the encouragement of my family.

When I started this book I was taking a break between researching a nonfiction project and documenting it in writing. I never did return to the task but the people who took the time to speak with me, experts in their fields, deserve recognition: So David Carrier, Paul Cartledge, Jane Dryden, Bernd Horn, Mandy-Rae Krack, Cynthia Pury, Alli Rainey, and Louise Wasylkiw, thank you. Stories don't appear in a vacuum, and our conversations—cowardice and bravery were frequent topics—occurred before I began this manuscript. Mark Adams and Keith Moses were also key contributors to that endeavour.

Thank you to Kevin Pecore for being the first to publish my fiction, and Breakwater Books for being the second. And my appreciation to Variant for help copyediting this work.

A big thanks to R. Wiens. He made a difference.

Peak would never have happened were it not for an entire sub-genre of nonfiction: mountaineering expedition accounts. I have read dozens over the years and they're almost all well-written and gripping. I will never stand atop K2 but I'm glad someone has and their story has been recorded.

Numerous sources offered inspiration for *Peak*: Dan Simmons's novel *The Terror*; Graham Bowley's account of the 2008 disaster on K2, *No Way Down*; and the documentary *Meru* are just a few.

I must mention Macleod Andrews. I was thrilled when I found out he was narrating *Peak*. Thank you, Macleod, for being the voice of my book.

My agent, David Fugate, is awesome. He worked with me from the first draft, played a key role in the development of the finished story—sometimes coach, sometimes editor—and was unwavering in his pursuit of publication. I am fortunate to have him in my corner.

The Podium Audio team deserves a huge thanks! I appreciate the faith you've put in this book, the time you've invested, and the care you've taken. I'm thrilled *Peak* found a home with you.

My daughter is a terrific person. Being her father has had an immensely positive effect on my life. She's funny and sharp and tremendously creative. I'm happy I have a book I can dedicate to her. I love you, kid.

Finally, my wife, Tanya. She valued my work even though it didn't pay bills. She was totally onboard when I devoted a year to the aforementioned nonfiction book, and never criticized me for not writing it. She's powerful and steady, empathetic and smart. And she was the one who first encouraged me to go to the mountains. My thanks and love.

ABOUT THE AUTHOR

Eric Sparling lives in Nova Scotia, Canada, with his wife and daughter. *Peak* is his second book.

DISCOVER
STORIES UNBOUND

PodiumAudio.com